D0810635

Creativity and Challenges in Chemical Engineering

Creativity and Challenges in Chemical Engineering

Three Lectures in Honor of Olaf Hougen

Given in the Department of Chemical Engineering University of Wisconsin–Madison

by

Robert C. Reid

1980–1981

First printing

Printed in the United States of America

Contents

Creativity and Challenges in Chemical Engineering

1

Supercritical-Fluid Extraction: A Perspective

Introduction

Supercritical-fluid (SCF) extraction is not unlike the common unit operation of liquid extraction; a fluid above its critical pressure and temperature is contacted with a solid or liquid mixture and extracts selectively one or more components. Interest in SCF extraction has stemmed from several advantages it may have over more conventional separation techniques:

1. It is often more efficient from the aspect of energy consumption—particularly when compared to distillation (Irani and Funk 1977).
2. The fluid solvent may be separated from the extracted solute by variations in either temperature or pressure, or both.
3. Nontoxic SCFs (such as the light hydrocarbons or CO_2) can often be employed.
4. The transport properties of an SCF lie between those of a liquid and a gas. Thus diffusion coefficients can be much larger than in liquid extraction systems.

HISTORICAL SUMMARY

The earliest SCF extraction experiments were conducted by Andrews (1887), who studied the solubility of liquid carbon dioxide in compressed nitrogen.* Shortly thereafter, Hannay and Hogarth (1879, 1880) found that the solubilities of crystalline I_2, KBr, $CoCl_2$, and $CaCl_2$ in supercritical ethanol were in excess of values predicted from the vapor pressures of the solutes modified by the Poynting correction. There have been many other studies since these pioneering papers; I summarize the available solid-fluid equilibrium references in Table 1.1. In most of the investigations until recently, emphasis was placed on developing phase diagrams for the fluid-solute systems investigated. The use of theory to correlate the experimental solubility data began with the application of the virial equation of state, but the principal object then was to employ the extraction data to determine interaction second virial coefficients (see, e.g., Baughman et al. 1975; Najour and King 1966, 1970; King and Robertson 1962). The use of equations-of-state to correlate solubilities is discussed later, and some comments are given relative to phase diagrams.

APPLICATIONS TO THE FOOD INDUSTRY

The most often cited example of SCF extraction in the food industry is the decaffeination of green-bean coffee (Zosel 1978). British and German patents have been issued (Hag Aktiengesellschaft 1974*b*; Vitzthum and Hubert 1975). While no data have been published, it is believed that supercritical CO_2 is relatively selective for caffeine.

A patent has also been issued to decaffeinate tea in a similar manner (Hag Aktiengesselschaft 1973*a*). SCFs have also been suggested to remove fats from foods, prepare spice extracts, make cocoa butter, and produce hop

*The paper describing Andrews' work was published after his death; the experiments were carried out in the 1870s.

extracts. These four applications are covered by patents of Hag Aktiengesellschaft. In all of these suggested processes, supercritical CO_2 is recommended as a nontoxic solvent that may be used in the temperature range where biological degradation is minimized.

It is suspected that extensive in-house, nonpublished research is being conducted by the major food industries.

OTHER APPLICATIONS

Hubert and Vitzthum (1978) suggested the use of supercritical CO_2 to separate nicotine from tobacco. Desalination of sea water by supercritical C_{11} and C_{12} paraffinic fractions has been successfully accomplished (Barton and Fenske 1970; Texaco 1967). Other applications include deasphalting of petroleum fractions with supercritical propane/propylene mixtures (Zhuze 1960), extraction of lanolin from wool fat (Peter et al. 1974), and the recovery of oil from waste gear oil (Studiengessellschaft Kohle, M.B.H. 1967). Holm (1975) discussed the use of supercritical CO_2 as a scavenging fluid in tertiary oil recovery. These and other processes are noted in reviews by Paul and Wise (1971), Wilke (1978), Irini and Funk (1977), and Gangoli and Thodos (1977).

SCF extraction in coal processing is being studied by a number of companies. In Great Britain, the National Coal Board has examined the de-ashing of coal with supercritical toluene and water (Bartle et al. 1975). The Kerr-McGee Company is said to have an operational process to de-ash coal using a proprietary solvent (Knebel and Rhodes 1978; Adams et al. 1978).

Modell and associates (1978, 1979) have proposed to regenerate activated carbon with supercritical CO_2.

Phase separations may be accomplished in some instances by contacting the liquid mixture with SCFs (Snedeker 1955; Elgin and Weinstock 1959; Newsham

Table 1.1. Summary of Previous Studies Using Supercritical Fluids

Solute	Solvent	$T(K)$	T_r(solvent)	P(bar)	P_r(solvent)	Reference
CO_2	Air	77–163	0.58–1.23	1–200	0.03–5.28	Webster 1950
CO_2	Air	115–150	0.87–1.13	4–49	0.11–1.29	Gratch 1945–46
Neopentane	Ar	199–258	1.32–1.71	NA		Baughman et al. 1975
Naphthalene	Ar	298–347	1.98–2.30	1–1100	0.02–22.57	King and Robertson 1962
CO	H_2	31–70	0.93–2.11	1–50	0.08–3.86	Dokoupel et al. 1955
N_2	H_2	25–70	0.75–2.11	1–50	0.08–3.86	Dokoupel et al. 1955
$CO+N_2$	H_2	35–66	1.05–1.99	5–15	0.39–1.16	Dokoupel et al. 1955
Xenon	H_2	155	4.67	4–8	0.31–0.62	Ewald 1955
CO_2	H_2	190	5.72	5–16	0.39–1.23	Ewald 1955
O_2	H_2	21–55	0.63–1.66	3–102	0.23–7.86	McKinley et al. 1962
Naphthalene	H_2	295–343	8.89–10.33	1–1100	0.08–84.81	King and Robertson 1962
C_2H_4	H_2	80–170	2.41–5.12	1–130	0.08–10.02	Hiza et al. 1968
Quartz	H_2O	653–698	1.01–1.08	300–500	1.36–2.27	Van Nieuwenburg and Van Zon 1935
Quartz	H_2O	423–873	0.65–1.35	1–1000	0–4.54	Jones and Staehle 1973
Na_2CO_3	H_2O	323–623	0.50–0.96	NA		Waldeck et al. 1932
$NA_2CO_3 + NaHCO_3$	H_2O	373–473	0.58–0.73	NA		Waldeck et al. 1932
UO_2	H_2O	773	1.19	1020	4.63	Morey 1957
Al_2O_3	H_2O	773	1.19	1020	4.63	Morey 1957
SnO_2	H_2O	773	1.19	1020	4.63	Morey 1957

Table 1.1—*Cont.*

Solute	Solvent	$T(K)$	T_r(solvent)	P(bar)	P_r(solvent)	Reference
NiO	H_2O	773	1.19	2040	9.25	Morey 1957
Nb_2O_5	H_2O	773	1.19	1020	4.63	Morey 1957
Ta_2O_5	H_2O	773	1.19	1020	4.63	Morey 1957
Fe_2O_3	H_2O	773	1.19	1020	4.63	Morey 1957
BeO	H_2O	773	1.19	1020	4.63	Morey 1957
GeO_2	H_2O	773	1.19	1020	4.63	Morey 1957
$CaSO_4$	H_2O	773	1.19	1020	4.63	Morey 1957
$BaSO_4$	H_2O	773	1.19	1020	4.63	Morey 1957
$PbSO_4$	H_2O	773	1.19	1020	4.63	Morey 1957
Na_2SO_4	H_2O	773	1.19	1020	4.63	Morey 1957
Silica	H_2O	883	1.36	1–1750	0–7.94	Kennedy 1950
Silica	H_2O	493–693	0.76–1.07	303	1.37	Kennedy 1944
Xenon	He	155	29.87	4–13	1.76–5.73	Ewald 1955
CO_2	He	190	36.61	4–9	1.76–3.96	Ewald 1955
Air	He	66.5–77.6	12.81–14.95	52–448	22.91–197.36	Zellner et al. 1962
Neopentane	He	199–258	38.34–49.71	NA		Baughman et al. 1975
Naphthalene	He	305–347	58.77–66.86	1–1100	0.44–485	King and Robertson 1962
Xenon	N_2	155	1.23	4–9.5	0.12–0.28	Ewald 1955
CO_2	N_2	140–190	1.11–1.51	5–100	0.15–2.95	Sonntag and Van Wylen 1962

(table continued on next page)

Table 1.1—*Cont.*

Solute	Solvent	$T(K)$	T_r(solvent)	P(bar)	P_r(solvent)	Reference
Neopentane	N_2	199–258	1.58–2.04	NA		Baughman et al. 1975
Naphthalene	N_2	295–345	2.34–2.73	1–1100	0.03–32.41	King and Robertson 1962
CH_4	Ne	44–91	0.99–2.05	10–100	0.36–3.63	Hiza and Kidnay 1966
Phenanthrene	CF_4	313	1.38	138–551	3.69–14.74	Eisenbeiss 1964
Naphthalene	CH_4	294–341	1.54–1.79	1–130	0.02–2.83	Najour and King 1966
Naphthalene	CH_4	296–348	1.55–1.83	1–1100	0.02–23.91	King and Robertson 1962
Anthracene	CH_4	339–458	1.78–2.40	1–100	0.02–2.17	Najour and King 1970
Neopentane	CH_4	199–258	1.04–1.35	NA		Baughman et al. 1975
Phenanthrene	CH_4	313	1.64	138–551	3.00–11.98	Eisenbeiss 1964
Naphthalene	C_2H_4	285–308	1.01–1.09	40–100	0.79–1.99	Diepen and Scheffer 1948*b*
Naphthalene	C_2H_4	318–338	1.13–1.18	40–270	0.79–5.36	Diepen and Scheffer 1953
Naphthalene	C_2H_4	296–308	1.05–1.09	1–130	0.02–2.58	Najour and King 1966
Naphthalene	C_2H_4	289.5–296.5	1.03–1.05	1–170	0.02–3.38	Van Gunst 1950
Naphthalene	C_2H_4	285–318	1.01–1.13	50–300	0.99–5.96	Tsekhanskaya et al. 1964
Anthracene	C_2H_4	338–453	1.20–1.60	1–100	0.02–1.99	Najour and King 1970
Anthracene	C_2H_4	323–358	1.14–1.27	103–480	2.04–9.53	Johnston and Eckert 1981
C_2Cl_6	C_2H_4	313–323	1.11–1.14	NA		Holder and Maass 1940
C_2Cl_6	C_2H_4	289.5–296.5	1.03–1.05	1–170	0.02–3.38	Van Gunst 1950
Naphthalene + C_2Cl_6	C_2H_4	289.5–296.5	1.03–1.05	1–170	0.02–3.38	Van Gunst 1950
p-Chloroiodobenzene	C_2H_4	286–305	1.01–1.08	21–101	0.42–2.01	Ewald et al. 1953

Table 1.1—*Cont.*

Solute	Solvent	$T(K)$	T_r(solvent)	P(bar)	P_r(solvent)	Reference
Phenanthrene	C_2H_4	313	1.11	138–551	2.74–10.94	Eisenbeiss 1964
Coal Tar	C_2H_4	298	1.06	310	6.16	Wise 1970
Anthracene	C_2H_6	336–448	1.10–1.47	1–100	0.02–2.05	Najour and King 1970
Naphthalene	C_2H_6	296–337	0.97–1.10	1–1100	0.02–22.52	King and Robertson 1962
Phenanthrene	C_2H_6	313	1.02	138–551	2.83–11.28	Eisenbeiss 1964
Naphthalene	CO_2	297–346	0.98–1.14	1–130	0.01–1.76	Najour and King 1966
Naphthalene	CO_2	308–328	1.01–1.08	60–330	0.81–4.47	Tsekhanskaya et al. 1964
Carbowax 4000	CO_2	313	1.03	300–2500	4.07–33.88	Czubryt et al. 1970
Carbowax 1000	CO_2	313	1.03	300–2500	4.07–33.88	Czubryt et al. 1970
1-Octadecanol	CO_2	313	1.03	300–2500	4.07–33.88	Czubryt et al. 1970
Stearic Acid	CO_2	313	1.03	300–2500	4.07–33.88	Czubryt et al. 1970
Phenanthrene	CO_2	313	1.03	138–551	1.87–7.47	Eisenbeiss 1964
Diphenylamine	CO_2	305–310	1.00–1.02	50–225	0.68–3.05	Tsekhansakaya et al. 1962
Phenol	CO_2	309–333	1.02–1.09	78–246	1.06–3.33	Van Leer and Paulaitis 1980
p-Chlorophenol	CO_2	309	1.02	79–237	1.06–3.21	Van Leer and Paulaitis 1980
2,4-Dichlorophenol	CO_2	309	1.02	79–203	1.06–2.75	Van Leer and Paulaitis 1980
Biphenyl	CO_2	308.3–328.5	1.02–1.08	105–484	1.42–6.56	McHugh and Paulaitis 1980

and Stigset 1978; Balder and Prausnitz 1966). The use of an SCF as the "third" component to a binary liquid mixture is analogous to the phase splits caused in salting-out processes. The advantages of the use of an SCF over a soluble solid relate to the ease whereby the supercritical fluid may be removed by a pressure reduction. A current commercial venture is exploiting this technology to separate ethanol-water mixtures (Krukonis, 1980).

To consider further the dehydration process, consider the phase diagram for water–methyl ethyl ketone–ethylene in Figure 1.1. While this diagram is drawn for an ethylene pressure slightly below the critical (T_c = 282.4 K, P_c = 50.4 bar), similar plots would be

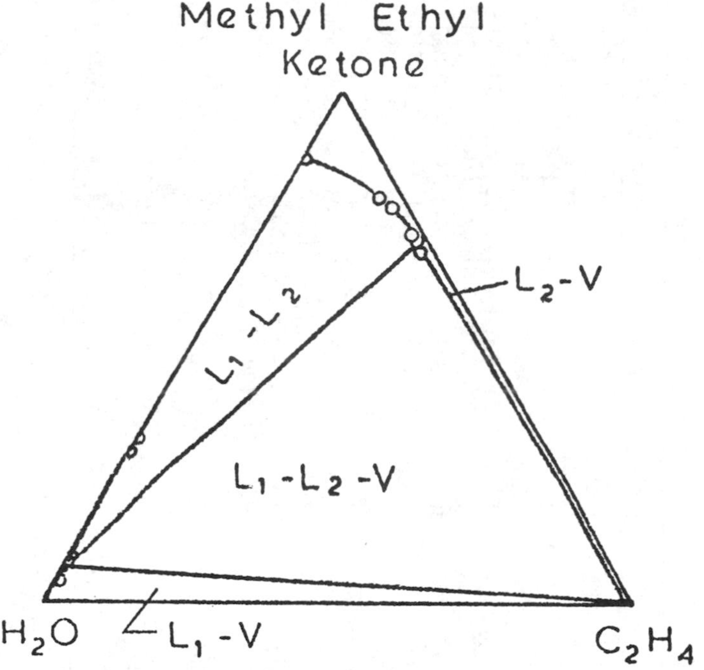

Figure 1.1—Phase equilibrium diagram for ethylene-water-methyl ethyl ketone at 35.5 bar and 288.1 K. Elgin and Weinstock 1959.

obtained at $P>P_c$. Note that a binary mixture of MEK shows a phasc split to a MEK-rich phase and a MEK-lean phase. If the MEK-rich phase were to be contacted with ethylene until the L_1-L_2-V region were reached, then there would be a different phase split with the MEK-rich phase containing very little water. Separation at high pressure with a subsequent pressure letdown to remove the ethylene leaves a rather dry MEK. The process flow sheet is given in Figure 1.2.

SUPERCRITICAL-FLUID CHROMATOGRAPHY

One quite promising application of SCF extraction is in chromatography. While no commercial equipment is yet available, several investigators have fabricated their own prototype units (Sie et al. 1966; van Wasen 1980; Klesper 1978). Due to the high operating pressures, there are significant problems in developing detectors and sample-injection techniques. The often drastic variation in solubility with pressure allows one to employ both tempera-

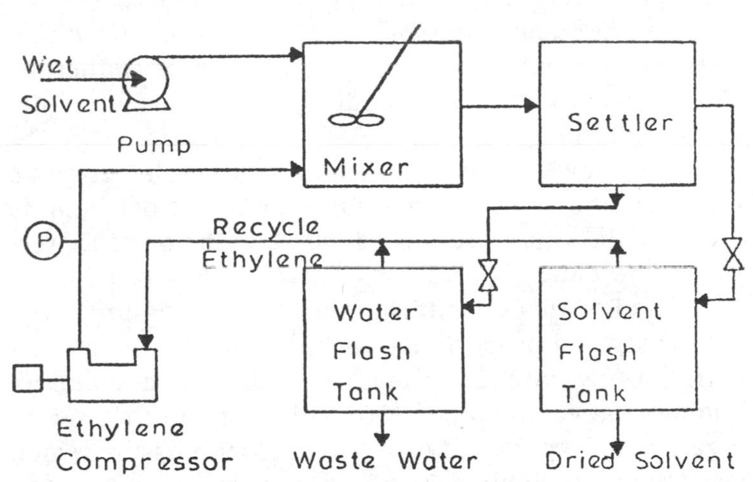

Figure 1.2—Schematic flowsheet for ethylene dehydration of solvents. Elgin and Weinstock 1959.

ture and pressure to optimize separations. Also, with the use of SCFs with low critical temperatures, it would appear that separations could be made of high molecular weight thermodegradable biological materials. Ionic species which decompose in gas chromatography have been stabilized in SCFs (Jentoft and Gouw 1972).

Finally, supercritical chromatography has been employed to obtain a variety of physical and thermodynamic properties for infinitely dilute systems—e.g., diffusion coefficients, activity coefficients, and interaction second virial coefficients (van Wasen 1980; Bartmann and Schneider 1973).

General Equilibrium Behavior

Before going into detail concerning experimental techniques to study solute-fluid behavior in SCFs, let us examine a general picture of the type of results as given in Figure 1.3. Here CO_2 is the supercritical fluid (T_c = 304.2 K, P_c = 72.8 bar), and solid benzoic acid is the solute. Experimental data points are shown for three isotherms, and the solid curves are predicted from theory, as described later.

At very low pressures, the fluid phase behaves as an ideal gas and the mole fraction benzoic acid is simply given by the vapor pressure divided by the system pressure. (The "ideal" gas curves shown on Figure 1.3 were calculated by this same technique for any pressure—i.e., y was assumed proportional to P^{-1} at any temperature.)

In the real case, as P increases, there is a solubility minimum at each temperature and, then, a dramatic increase in y. Experimental data in the low-pressure region are difficult to obtain because of the very low concentrations. While not shown, y does pass through a maximum with pressure and then again decreases.

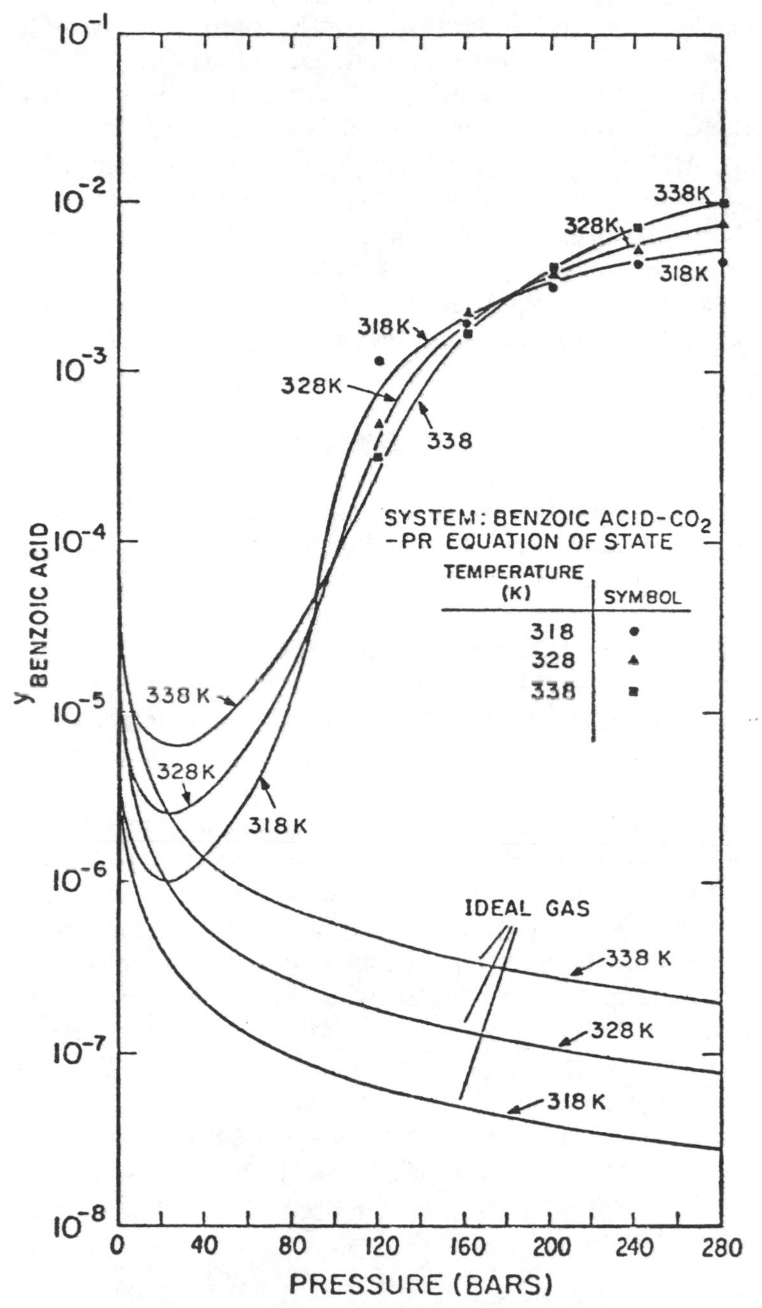

Figure 1.3—Solubility of benzoic acid in CO_2.

The effect of temperature is most interesting. At both low and high pressures, an increase in temperature leads to an increase in solubility. At intermediate pressures, there is a region of "retrograde" precipitation where a temperature increase causes a reduction in solubility. Thus solubility becomes a rather complex function of both pressure and temperature. Finally, if, at any particular temperature, one divides the real solubility by the ideal gas value, the ratio is termed the *enhancement* factor. As is rather obvious, these can be quite large.

Phase Diagrams

The phase behavior for a solid solute in contact with an SCF is of considerable importance in providing guidance to possible operating regimes.

To establish a basis and to define certain terms, examine a rather simple system of a binary of 1 and 2 as shown in Figure 1.4. Component 1 has a higher melting point than 2 and is less volatile at any given temperature. In Figure 1.4 *KB* and *HA* represent the solid-gas equilibrium curves for pure 1 and 2, respectively. The triple points for 1 and 2 are shown by *B* and *A*. The line *CDEF* is a eutectic line for an equilibrium condition of pure solid 1 (*F*), pure solid 2 (*C*), a saturated liquid (*E*), and a saturated vapor (*D*). This is an invariant state. At pressures higher than the eutectic pressure, the T-x_1 projection is shown at the top. We see the usual solubility curves with the "eutectic point" projected as E'. At temperatures below the eutectic, no liquid phase exists, and a P-x_1 projection is given in the front plane. The area bounded by *GHI* represents a two-phase region of solid 2 with gas. Similarly, *IJK* refers to solid 1-gas. *K* and *H* are the sublimation pressures of solids 1 and 2 at the temperature shown.

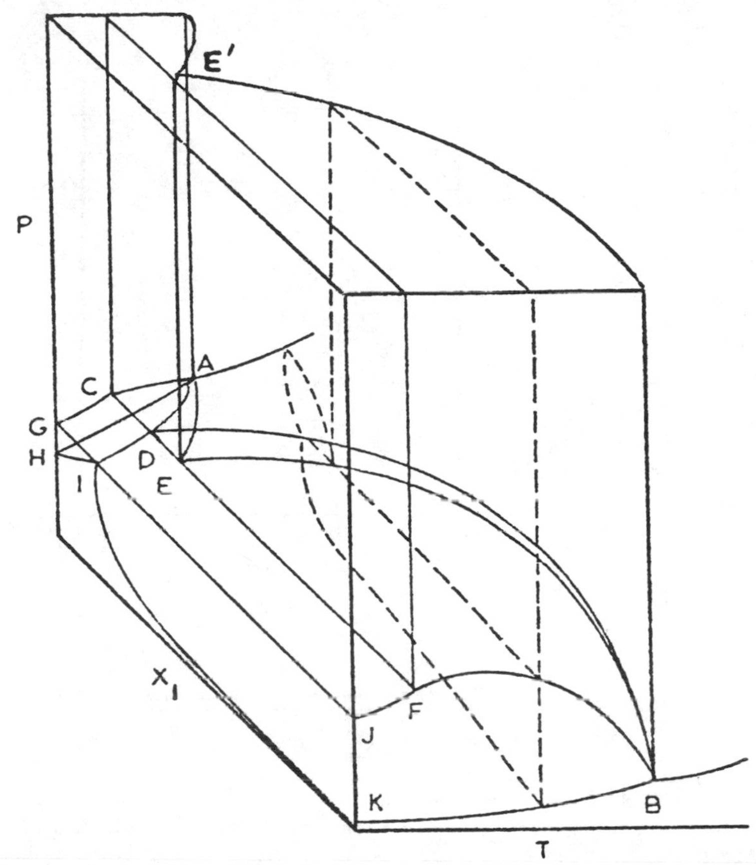

Figure 1.4—The pressure-temperature-composition surfaces for the equilibrium between two pure solid phases, a liquid phase and a vapor phase. Rowlinson and Richardson 1959.

More pertinent to the problem of interest are cases where the system temperature exceeds the triple point of 2 (*A*). A P-x_1 projection in this region is shown as the dashed isothermal cut in Figure 1.4 and redrawn in Figure 1.5. At the pressure corresponding to *X*, *Y*, and *Z*, we have three phases in equilibrium, gas, liquid, and solid-1. This is one pressure and temperature for the "three-phase" locus.

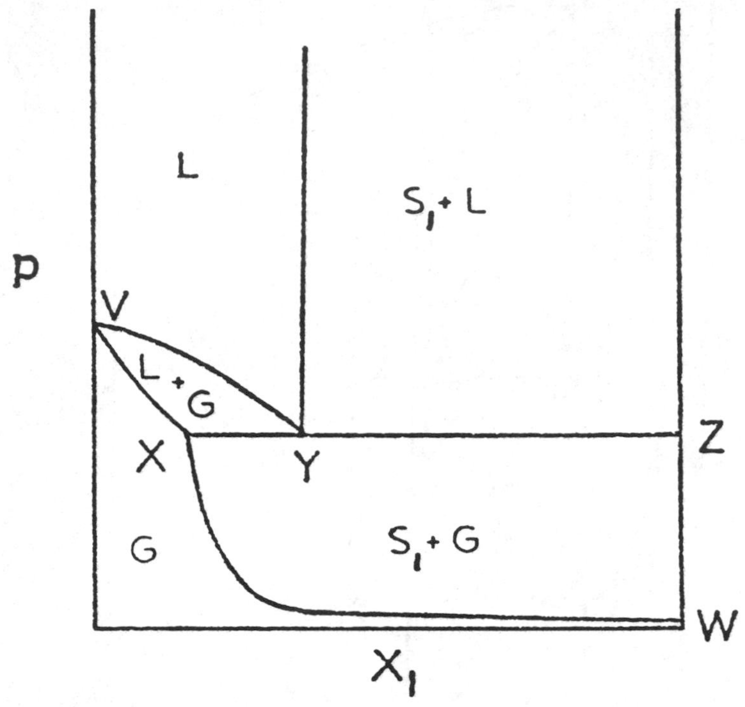

Figure 1.5—A pressure composition section at a constant temperature lying between the melting points of the pure components. Rowlinson and Richardson 1959.

Not shown in Figure 1.4 are the critical points of 1 and 2. They are off the drawing at much higher temperatures.

Collapsing the plot of 1.4 to a *P-T* projection—and including the usual critical locus—one has Figure 1.6. *KB* and *HA* are (as in Fig. 1.4) the sublimation curves of pure 1 and 2, and again, *B* and *A* are the triple points for these pure materials. *N* and *M* represent the critical points for 1 and 2, and it is assumed that the critical locus is continuous between these end points. The curve *BF* is the projection of curve *BE* in Figure 1.4, while *AC* is the projection of curve AE. At any temperature above T_A, there is a single pressure on A-(C,F)-B, and this represents one point on the three-phase locus as shown in Figure 1.5 (X-Y-Z). At points C, F in Figure 1.6, we have the quadruple invariant point, while between $T_{C,F}$ and T_A, we have two different states for the three-phase locus, one near pure 2 and one closer to pure 1. Note also that the three-phase locus has a definite convex bow. This effect is important for binary systems where one component is very much less volatile than the other. In this case, the three-phase curves may bow to such an extent as to "cut" the critical locus, as illustrated schematically in Figure 1.7.

The points of intersection are termed critical end points with p being the lower and q the upper critical end points. Since the domain below the three-phase locus in

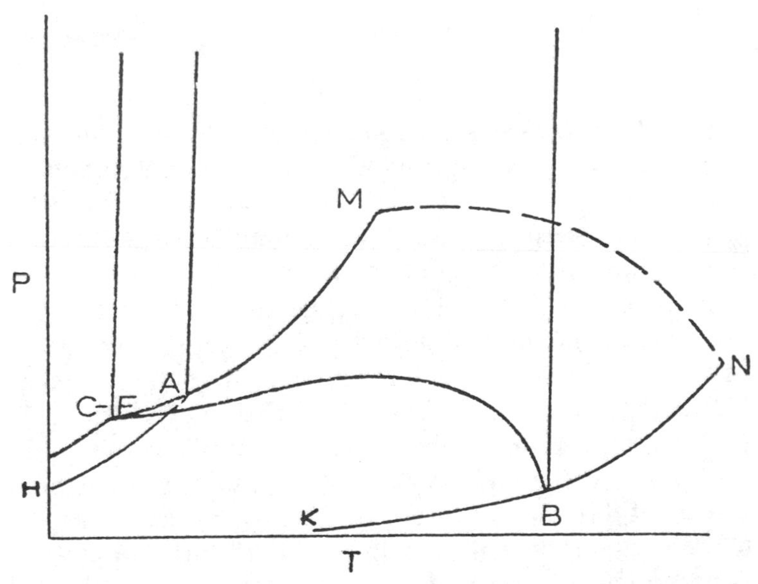

Figure 1.6—*P-T* projection of a system in which the three-phase line does not cut the critical locus.

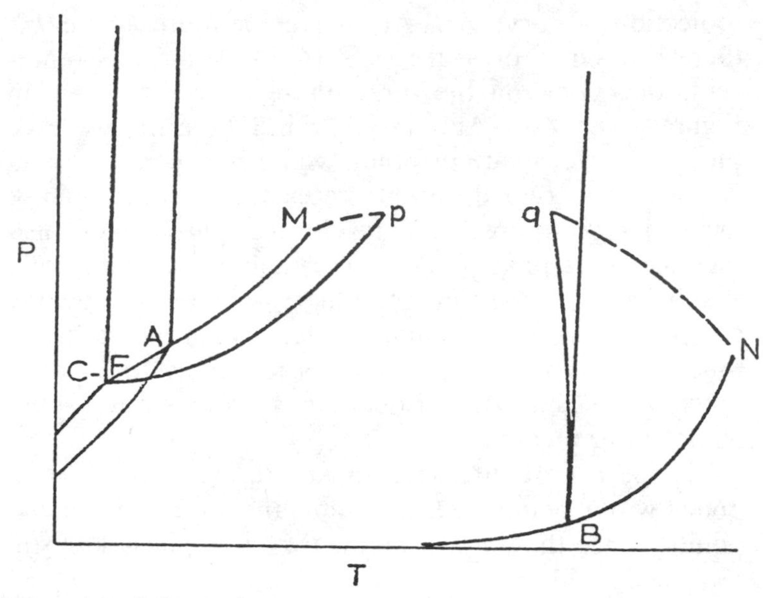

Figure 1.7—*P-T* projection of a system in which the three-phase line cuts the critical locus.

Figure 1.6 represents an equilibrium between solid and gas, the cutting of the critical locus effectively opens a window for solid-gas (or solid-fluid) equilibria. In other words, between T_p and T_q one may have solid-fluid equilibrium with no liquid phase present.

To take a more specific case, the system naphthalene-ethylene is shown in Figure 1.8. For this system, T_p is about 11° C and is not shown, as our interest lies at higher temperatures. T_q has been found to be about 52.1° C (174 atm, and at a mole fraction naphthalene of 0.17 ± 0.005; van Welie and Diepen 1961). Consider a *P-x* projection of this binary system at 35° C. Points along the 35° C projection represent naphthalene concentrations in the supercritical ethylene (T_c = 9° C, P_c = 49 atm) in the presence of solid naphthalene. At low pressure, little

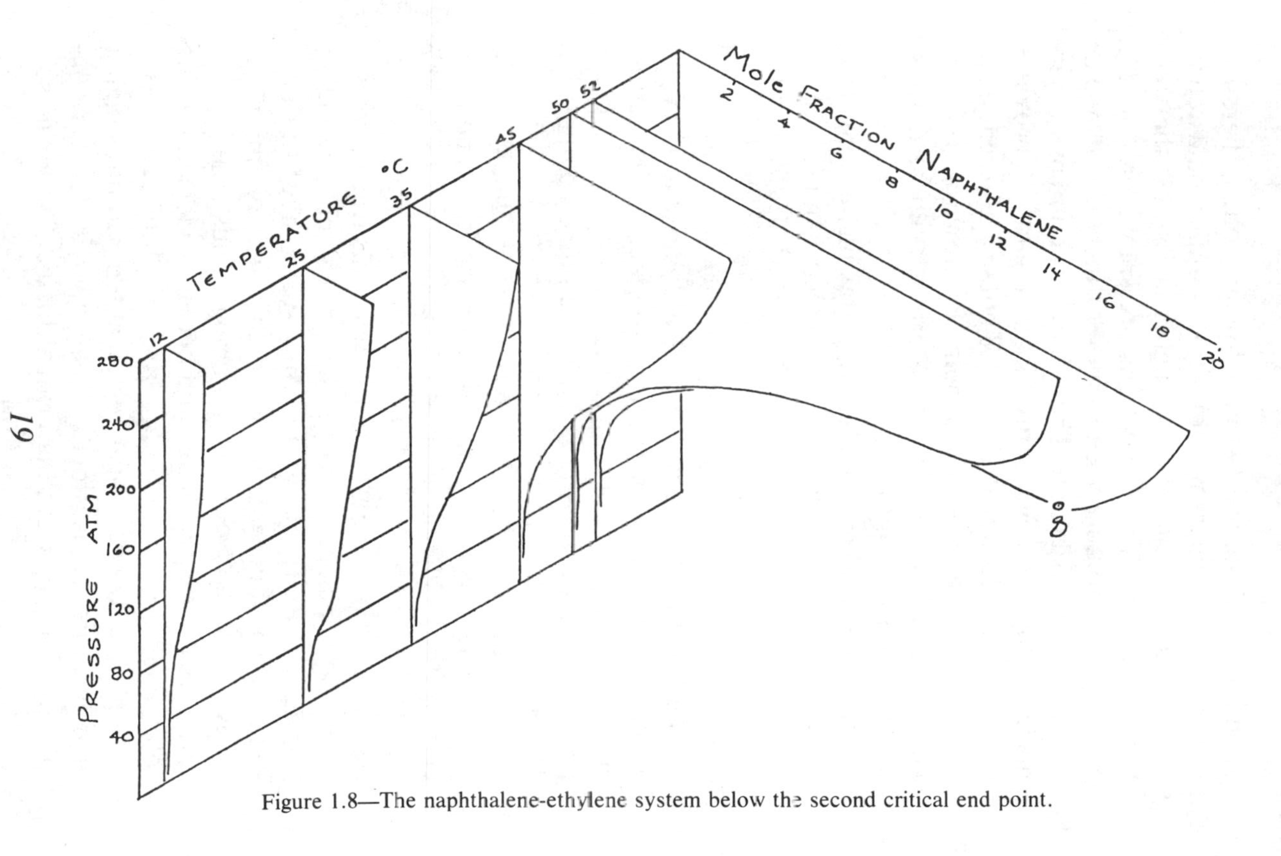

Figure 1.8—The naphthalene-ethylene system below the second critical end point.

naphthalene dissolves. (At very low pressures, there is a "floor" to the diagram—not shown—that would represent a homogeneous gas.) At higher pressures, the solubility increases. The projections are shown only to 280 atm, but the solubility continues to increase at higher pressures—up to a point. The "fine" structure of isothermal *P-x* projections is covered later. Figure 1.3 provides the same information as Figure 1.8 but in a different manner. The upper critical end point is shown as point *q*; note that the solubility increases dramatically as the system temperature approaches T_q.

An isometric sketch including states higher than T_q is shown in Figure 1.9. At the extreme left-hand side of the drawing, a *P-x* projection is shown at 35° C. This is the same one as described above for Figure 1.8.

The upper critical end point is shown in Figure 1.9 at the intersection between the critical locus and the solid naphthalene-liquid-gas three-phase locus. This curve starts at the triple point of naphthalene and runs to higher pressures until it ends at *q*. Only the liquid composition on the three-phase locus is shown.

A section is shown at 50 mole percent (liquid) naphthalene which is higher than the upper critical end point composition. (The point on the three-phase locus at 50% naphthalene is at $T \sim 57.4°$ C, $P \sim 93$ atm). For this section, a sharply rising trace is shown. This trace attempts to portray a plane, nearly vertical, but slanting to higher temperatures that yield the solid naphthalene-supercritical fluid equilibria. To the right of this plane (above the $L + G$ surface), a homogeneous fluid is present. This trace approaches and becomes identical to the solid-liquid dividing locus for 100% naphthalene.

There is also a liquid-gas region at temperatures higher than the three-phase locus. The upper surface is continuous and intersects the critical locus. The lower sur-

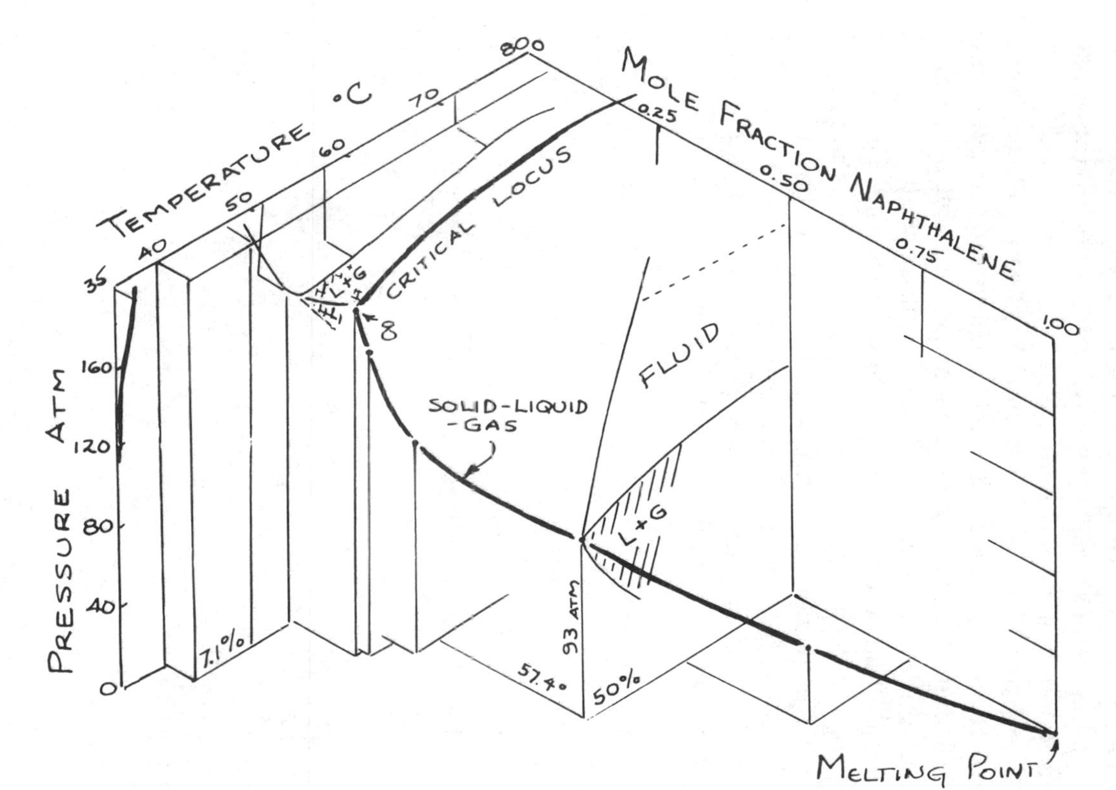

Figure 1.9—The naphthalene-ethylene system above the second critical end point.

face is not shown but would lead, at low pressure, to a homogeneous gas region. A better view of the cross-section is given in Figure 1.10.

Also in Figure 1.9 an attempt has been made to show a section at about 7.1% naphthalene, a value below the second critical end point concentration. A clearer section of this same region is given in Figure 1.10. Now, the solid-fluid equilibrium curve falls with increasing temperature until it reaches a minimum (at temperatures close to T_q). For higher temperatures, a liquid appears.

Thus, from Figures 1.8 through 1.10, it can be seen that when operating below T_q (and above T_p), one may have an equilibrium system of solid naphthalene and a naphthalene-ethylene fluid phase. Concentrations of naphthalene are normally low unless the pressure is high and/or the temperature near T_q. It is possible, however, to have a solid-supercritical equilibria above T_q at high pressures.

Figure 1.11 shows a *P-T* projection for the ethylene-naphthalene system from van Welie and Diepen (1961).

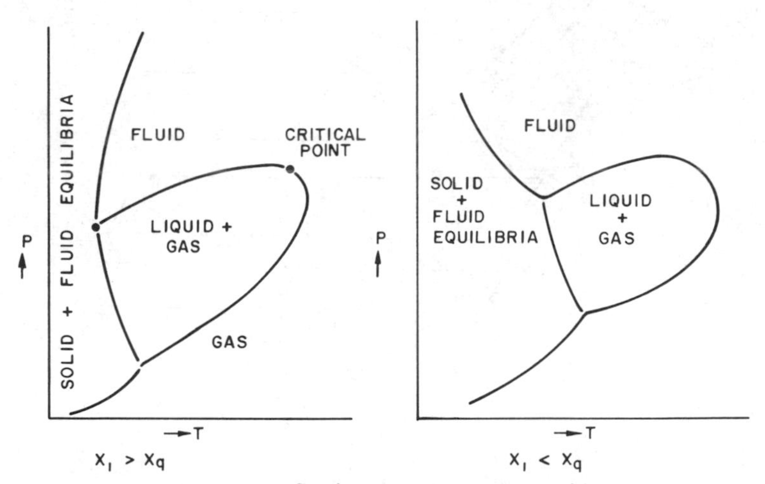

Figure 1.10—Sections at constant composition.

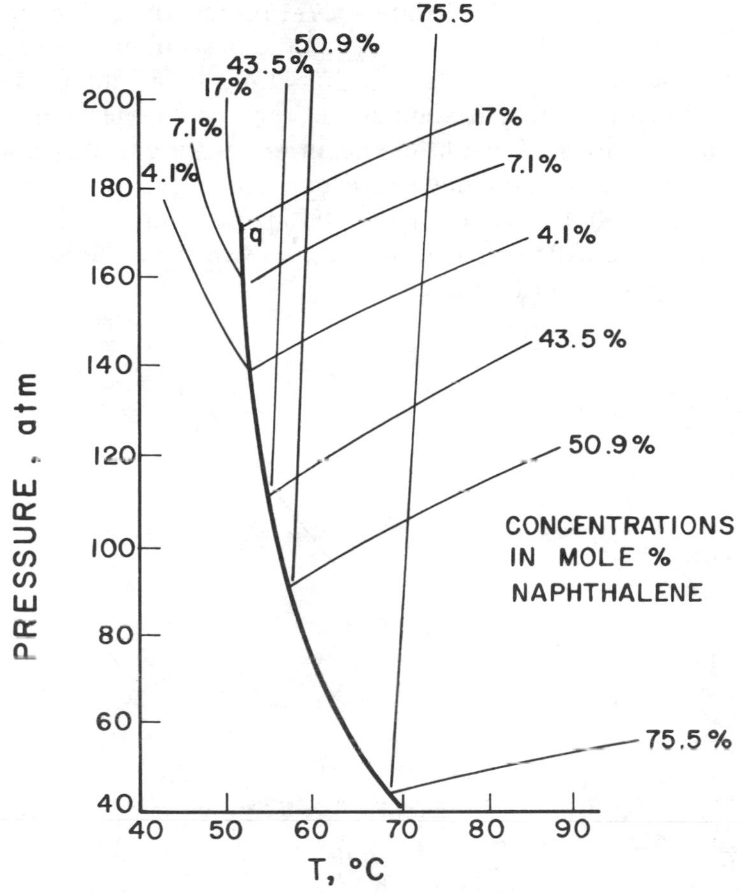

Figure 1.11—*P-T* projection for the naphthalene-ethylene system.

Naphthalene concentrations both below and above the value of x_q (17 mole percent) are shown. For each concentration trace on the left branch, the solid-fluid equilibrium domain is defined. For the branch on the right, the liquid-gas equilibrium is delineated. Intersection of two curves (both of the right hand branch) would delineate the composition of the liquid and vapor in equilibrium.

Finally, Figure 1.12 shows a T-x projection at 270 atm (274 bar). This pressure exceeds the maximum pressure on the critical locus (about 227 atm), so no liquid-gas region is shown. The solid circles represent experimental compositions of naphthalene in supercritical ethylene when solid naphthalene is present. The curve terminates at about 90° C, the estimated melting point of pure naphthalene at 270 atm. The solid curve was estimated from theory as described later.

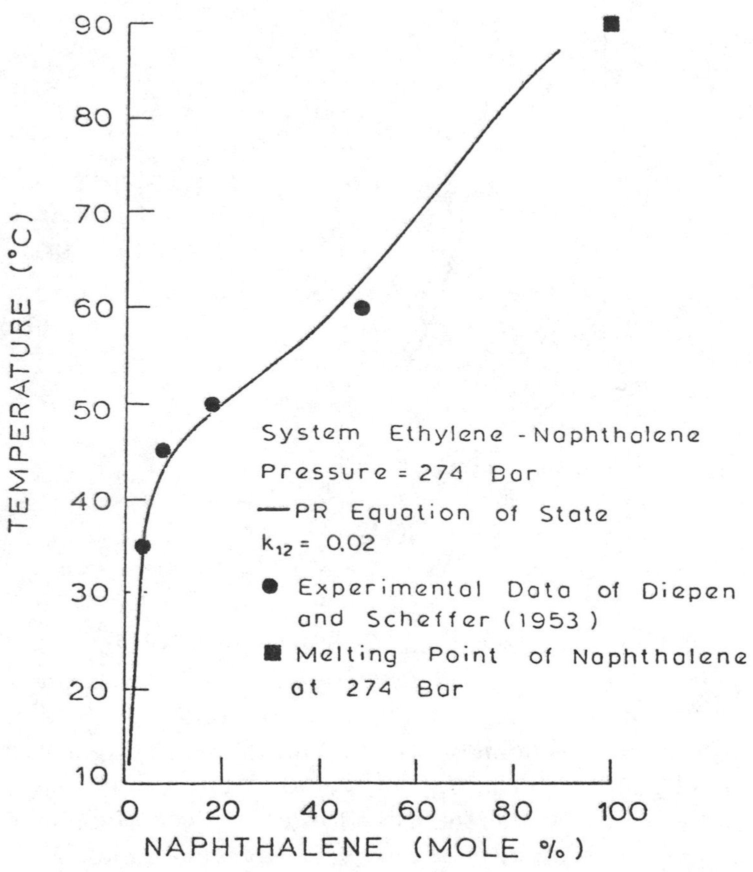

Figure 1.12—Solubility of naphthalene in ethylene at high temperatures.

Experimental equilibrium studies are typically carried out in a flow system. The equipment used in our laboratory is shown in Figure 1.13. CO_2 or ethylene were the supercritical fluids, and we have studied a number of solid solutes and solute mixtures. The gas, after compression, was passed through a temperature-controlled extractor packed with layers of glass wool and solute. Precipitation occurred after expansion of the fluid mixture to one bar. The solute was trapped in cold U-tubes and weighed. The volume of CO_2 or ethylene used was determined with a calibrated dry-test meter.

Experiments were conducted to insure that the technique would provide accurate and reliable equilibrium solubilities. The most important test was to run with the system naphthalene-carbon dioxide so as to compare the measured values of naphthalene solubility with those of Tsekhanskaya and associates (1964). When the equilibrium solubilities were compared with these data, the average deviation was only 1.3%.

We also carried out tests for long times but separated the run into several periods. At the start of each period, new (tared) U-tubes were inserted and the previous tubes removed. No change in equilibrium concentration was noted when data from the different time periods were compared.

We also carried out repeat tests (for naphthalene-CO_2) in which we varied the position of the solid in the extractor, i.e., data were obtained with the solid distributed evenly in layers over the entire height (the usual mode), with the solid only in the lower half, and with the solid only in the top half. Identical results were obtained for all tests at the same temperature and pressure. These results indicated that the extractor was isothermal and also that equilibrium was rapidly attained.

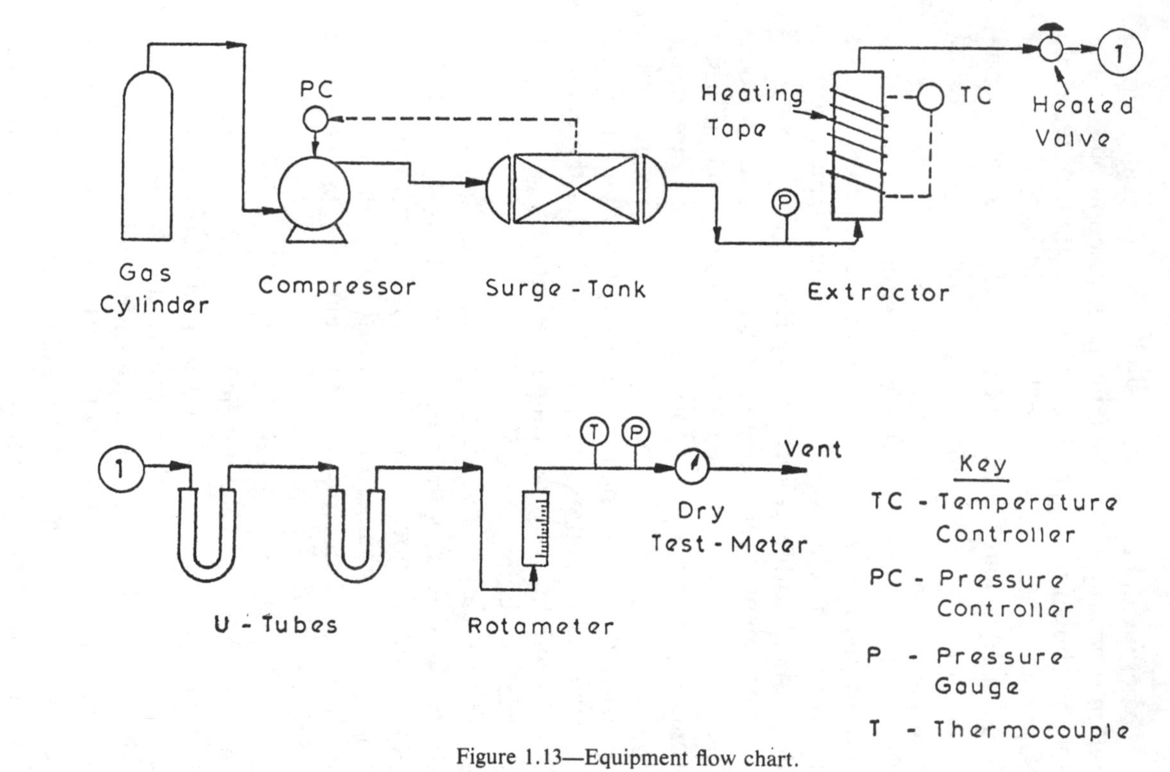

Figure 1.13—Equipment flow chart.

Tests were also run in which the flow rate was varied from 0.036 to 0.13 standard m^3/hr. No effect was noted in the outlet concentration of naphthalene, and this reinforces our conclusion that equilibrium was rapidly achieved.

Some typical results are shown in Figures 1.14 and

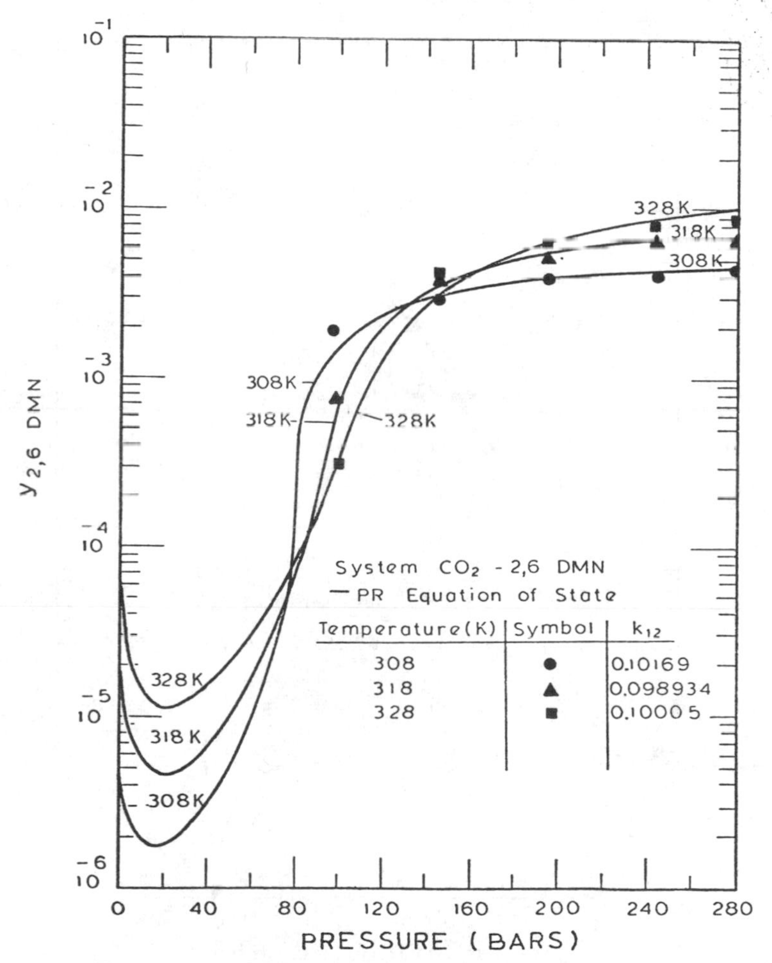

Figure 1.14—Solubility of 2,6-dimethyl naphthalene in CO_2.

1.15 for the systems CO_2-2,6-dimethyl naphthalene (DMN) and ethylene-DMN. Each system was studied at three temperatures, 308 K, 318 K, and 328 K. The general shape of the curves is quite similar to the CO_2-benzoic acid case given earlier in Figure 1.3. We also studied mixtures of solid solutes, but before presenting these re-

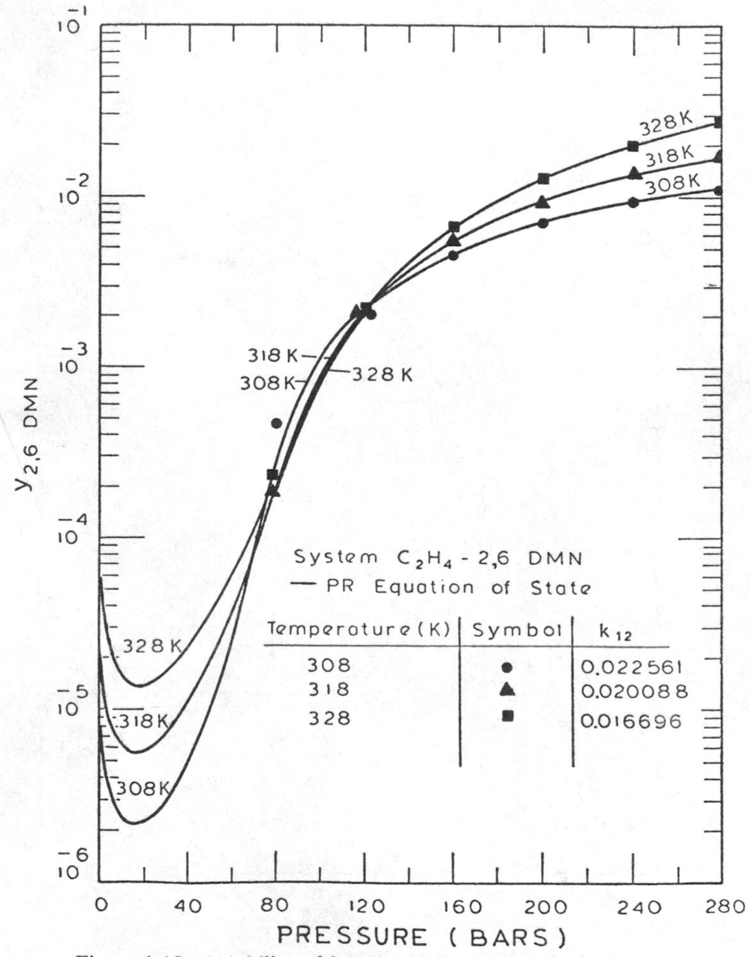

Figure 1.15—Solubility of 2,6-dimethyl naphthalene in ethylene.

sults, I would like to review briefly the thermodynamic method we used to correlate the solubility data.

Thermodynamic Analysis

The thermodynamics applicable to relate the equilibrium mole fraction of a solute dissolved in a high pressure gas (fluid) have been treated earlier by Prausnitz (1969). The results may be written in a deceptively simple form. With 1 representing the solute which is present both as a pure solid and is dissolved in the fluid phase,

$$y_1 = (P_{vp_1}/P)(1/\phi_1) \exp [(V_1/RT)(P-P_{vp_1})] \quad (1.1)$$

with y_1 the fluid phase mole fraction of 1.

In equation (1.1) it has been assumed that (*a*) the fluid phase component does not dissolve in the solid, (*b*) the molar volume of the solid is independent of pressure, and (*c*) the fugacity coefficient of pure vapor 1 at T, P_{vp_1} is unity. In most instances, these three assumptions are satisfactory.

The only term on the right-hand side of eq. (1.1) which reflects the fact that the fluid phase is a mixture is the fugacity coefficient of component 1, ϕ_1. Accurate estimates of this variable are necessary to determine y_1. ϕ_1 can be found from an applicable mixture equation of state using well-known thermodynamics. We have employed, primarily, the Peng-Robinson (1976) modifications of the Redlich-Kwong equation of state (1949).

$$ln\phi_i = \frac{b_i}{b}(Z-1) - ln(Z-B) - \frac{A}{2\sqrt{2}B}$$

$$x \left\{ 2\sum_j (1 - k_{ij}) \frac{[a_i(T)a_j(T)]^{1/2}}{a(T)} y_j - \frac{b_i}{b} \right\}$$

$$1n \left(\frac{Z + 2.414B}{Z - 0.414B} \right) \quad (1.2)$$

In this equation Z is the compressibility factor of the gas mixture and is found from the original equation of state,

$$Z^3 - (1 - B)Z^2 + (A - 3B^2 - 2B)Z - (AB - B^2 - B^3) = 0 \quad (1.3)$$

To calculate ϕ, or Z, pure component parameters a_i and b_i are found from eqs. (1.4) and (1.6) using critical properties and acentric factors.

$$a_i = \Omega_a \frac{R^2 T_{c_i}^2}{P_{c_i}} \left[1 + \kappa_i (1 - T_{r_i}^{1/2}) \right]^2 \quad (1.4)$$

where

$$\kappa_i = 0.37464 + 1.54226\omega_i - 0.26992\omega_i^2 \quad (1.5)$$

$$b_i = \Omega_b \frac{R T_{c_i}}{P_{c_i}} \quad (1.6)$$

Mixing parameters a and b are related to the pure component terms a_i and b_i as

$$a = \sum_i \sum_j x_i x_j a_i^{1/2} a_j^{1/2} (1 - k_{ij}) \quad (1.7)$$

$$b = \sum_i x_i b_i \quad (1.8)$$

Variables A and B as used in eqs. (1.2) and (1.3) are defined by

$$A = \frac{aP}{R^2 T^2} \quad (1.9)$$

$$B = \frac{bP}{RT} \quad (1.10)$$

The interaction parameter k_{ij} is characteristic of a binary pair (i and j) and is normally assumed to be independent of pressure, composition, or temperature. As will be seen later, however, we did find a weak temperature effect on k_{ij}.

Estimated solute mole fractions are shown in Figures 1.3, 1.14, and 1.15 as the solid curves. The interaction parameter employed is also shown. In general, the Peng-Robinson equation of state well correlates the data.

Figure 1.16 also shows estimated solubilities of naphthalene in nitrogen at high pressures and at ambient temperatures. Here, nitrogen is at a very high T_r (~2.5) and is close to an ideal gas. There is little effect of pressure on solubility.

Solid Mixtures

We have also measured the solubilities of a few solid mixtures in both supercritical CO_2 and ethylene. In all

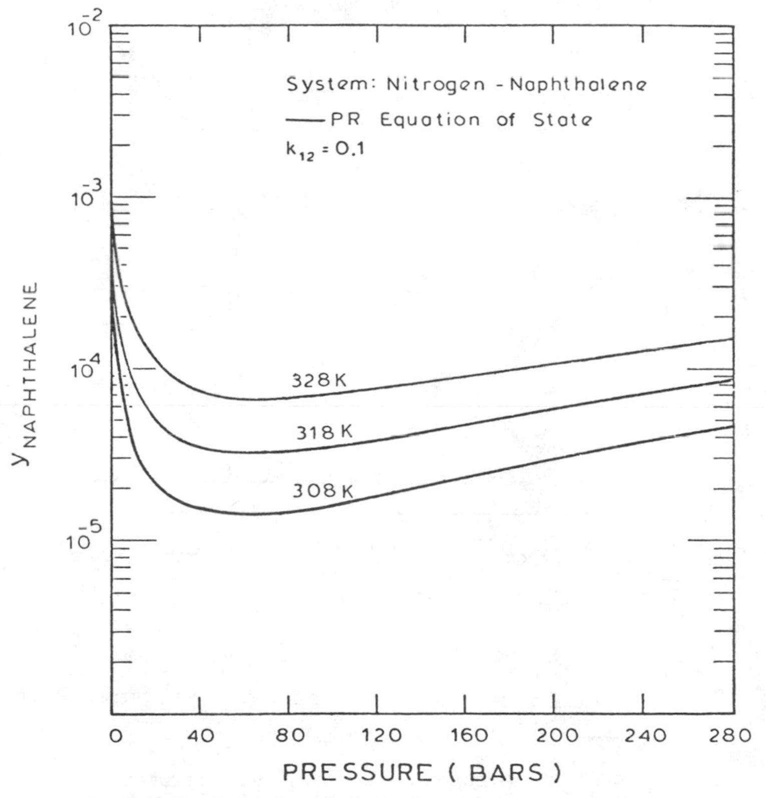

Figure 1.16—Solubility of naphthalene in compressed nitrogen.

cases we first determined the eutectic curve for the binary solute pair to assure ourselves that no solid solutions were formed. Figure 1.17 shows data for the solute binary phenanthrene-naphthalene system. The solid curves were calculated assuming these two solids formed an ideal solution.

In the actual experiments, we used simple granulated physical mixtures of the two solutes, and in other cases, we melted the solutes and allowed these to crystallize. The solid, after grinding, was also extracted. No differ-

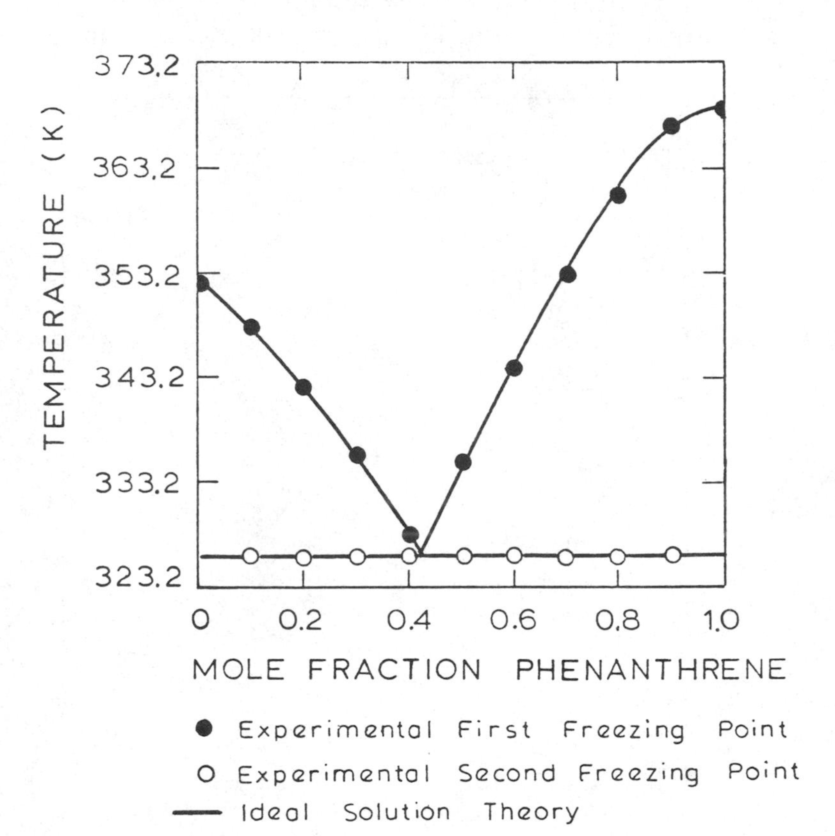

Figure 1.17—Phenanthrene-naphthalene freezing curves.

ence in results was noted for runs carried out in these two different modes.

In Figures 1.18 and 1.19 we show the solubilities of both naphthalene ($C_{10}H_8$) and phenanthrene ($C_{14}H_{10}$) in CO_2 and compare solubilities for each pure solute. Note

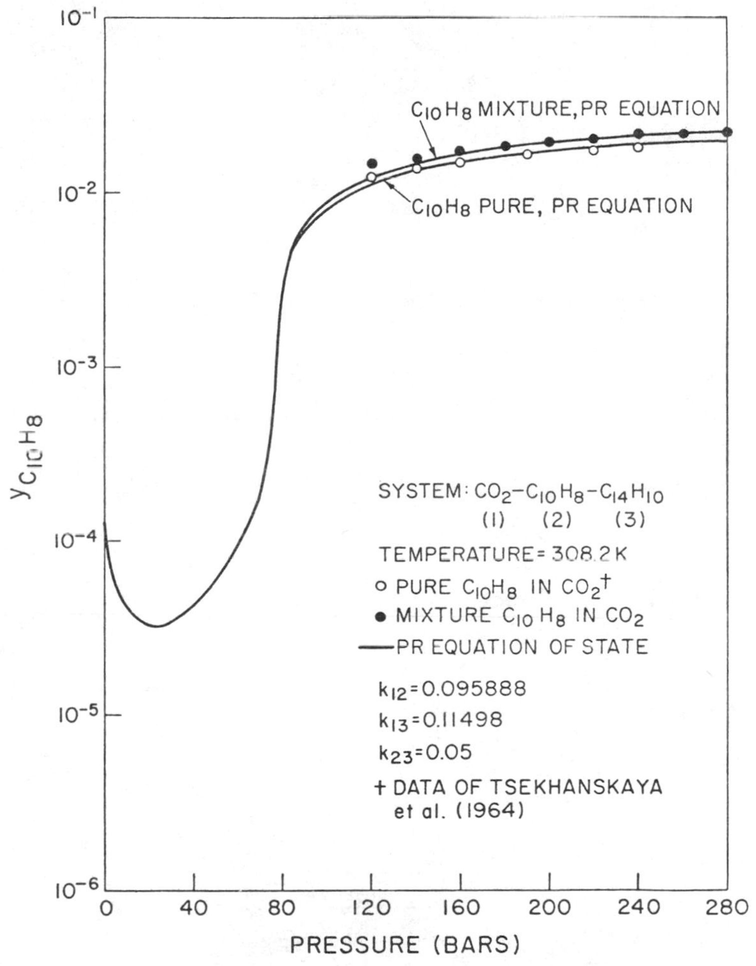

Figure 1.18—Naphthalene solubility in a ternary system.

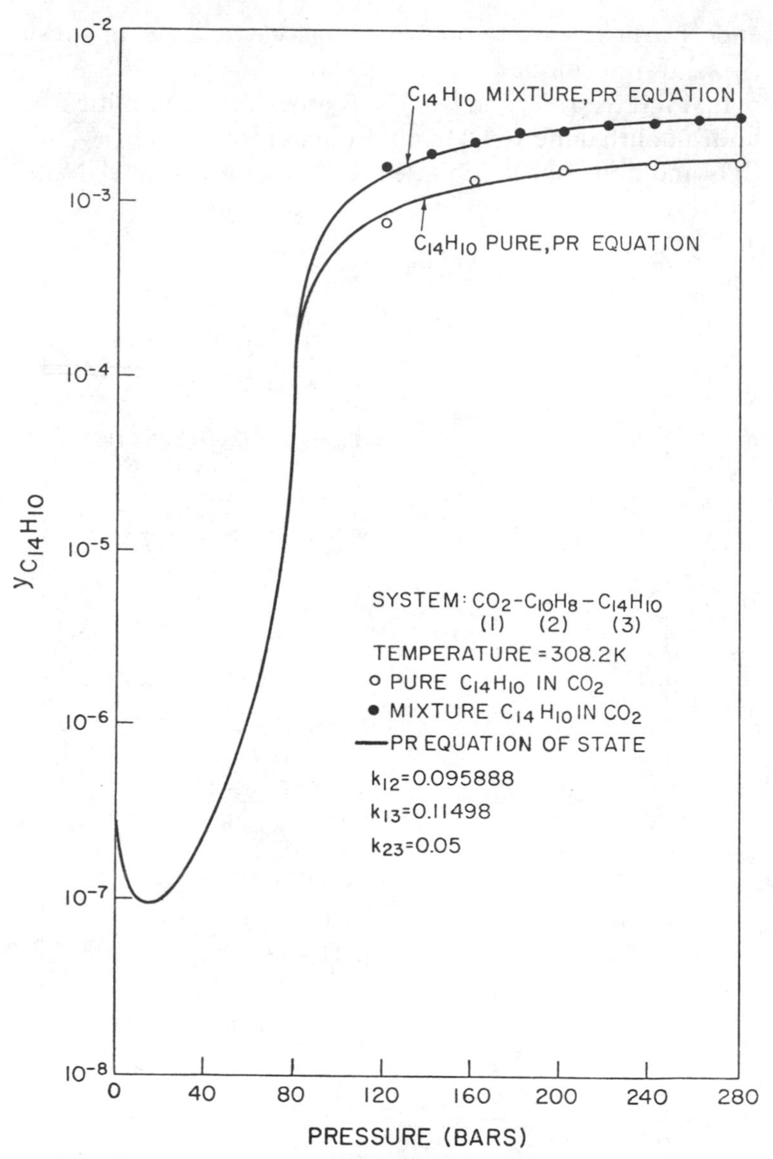

Figure 1.19—Phenanthrene solubility in a ternary system.

that the presence of about 1% naphthalene *increases* the phenanthrene concentration by a significant amount. The mixture naphthalene concentrations are only slightly higher than the pure solute values. Similar increases were found for benzoic acid (280% increase)-naphthalene (100% increase), and for 2,3-dimethylnaphthalene (140% increase)-naphthalene (50% increase).

The only other data in the literature for binary solute solubilities were reported by Van Gunst (1950) for the system hexachloroethane-naphthalene-ethylene. His data are shown in Figures 1.20 and 1.21. Both solute solubilities increase by about 300% relative to values for pure solutes.

The Peng-Robinson equation of state also worked well to correlate the binary solute data, but a solute-solute interaction parameter had to be included. Note the solute-SCF interaction parameters were determined from pure solute-fluid data.

Selectivities (α) for the naphthalene-phenanthrene-CO_2 system are given in Figure 1.22. At one bar, the selectivity is essentially the ratio of solute vapor pressures. Increasing the pressure dramatically reduces α, and a relatively constant value is achieved at high pressures.

The enhancement of solute solubilities by small changes in vapor phase compositions is quite interesting and relates to the "entrainer" concept to be discussed later.

Solubility Maxima

Our experimental data (and those of most others in the field) extend only to about 300–400 bar.

It is interesting, however, to employ a computer simulation to even higher pressures. The results of such calculations are shown in Figure 1.23 for the solubilities of naphthalene in supercritical ethylene for pressures up to 4 kbar and for several temperatures. Experimental data are shown only for the 285 K isotherm to indicate the range covered and the applicability of the Peng-

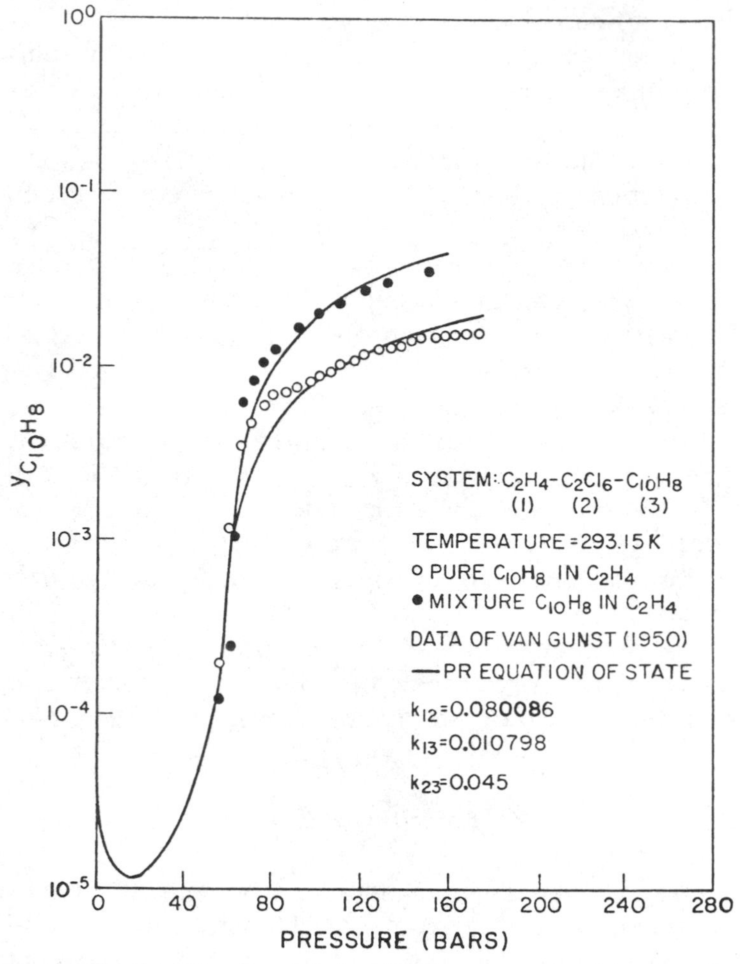

Figure 1.20—Solubility of naphthalene in a ternary system. Data from Van Gunst 1950.

Robinson equation. (The values of the interaction parameter, k_{ij}, in this equation were found from regressing the experimental solubility data for four isotherms and averaging the results. Over the temperature range studied, an average interaction parameter correlates

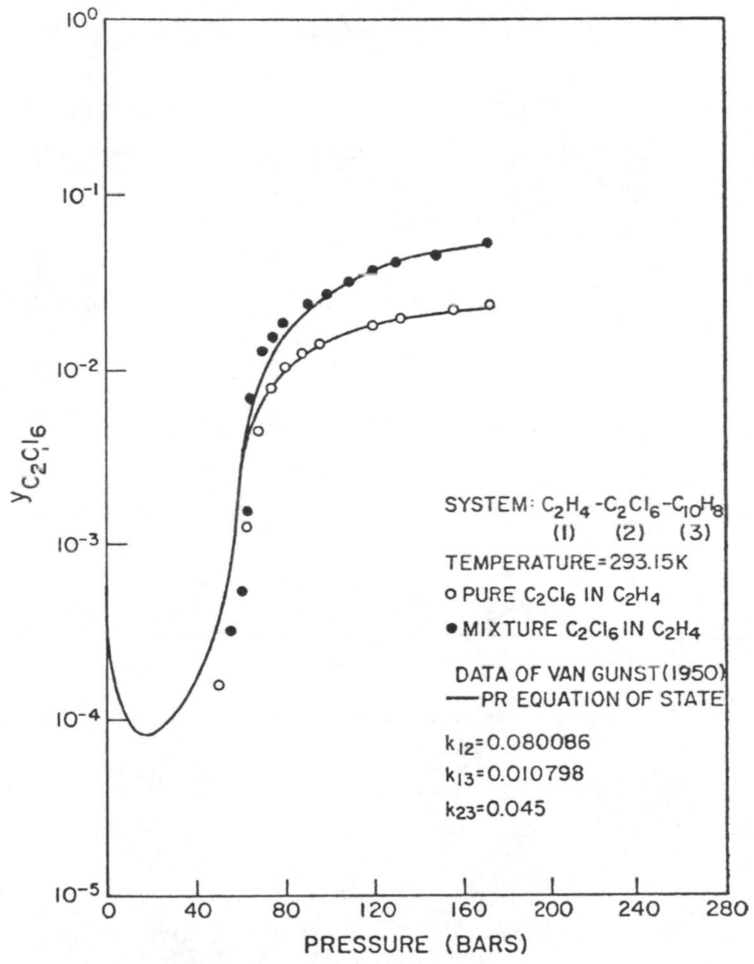

Figure 1.21—Solubility of hexachloroethane in a ternary system. Data from Van Gunst 1950.

isothermal solubility data at most 4% different than when using a temperature-dependent interaction parameter.

For the naphthalene-ethylene system, the solubility attains a minimum value in the range of 15 to 20 bar and a maximum at several hundred bar. The minimum concentration is of interest to those who wish to purify a gas from a volatile impurity by compression and condensa-

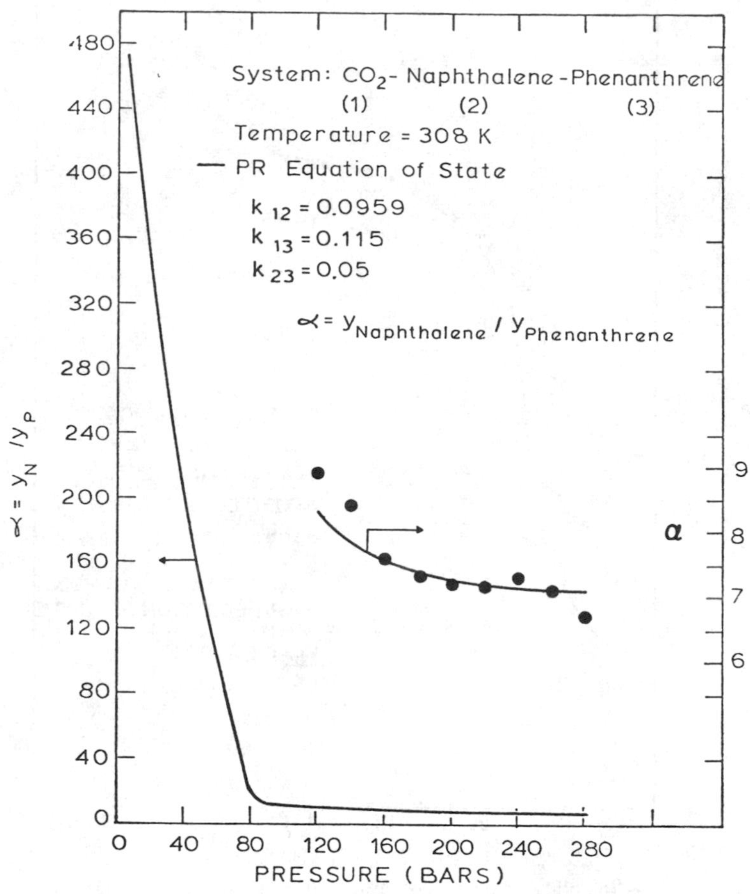

Figure 1.22—Selectivity for the naphthalene-phenanthrene-CO_2 system.

tion. (See Hinckley and Reid 1964.) The maximum concentration of solute is clearly of concern to those who would like to employ SCFs to extract a solute into the fluid phase.

The existence of the concentration maxima for the naphthalene-ethylene system is confirmed by considering the earlier work by Van Welie and Diepen. They also graphed the mole fraction of naphthalene in ethylene as a

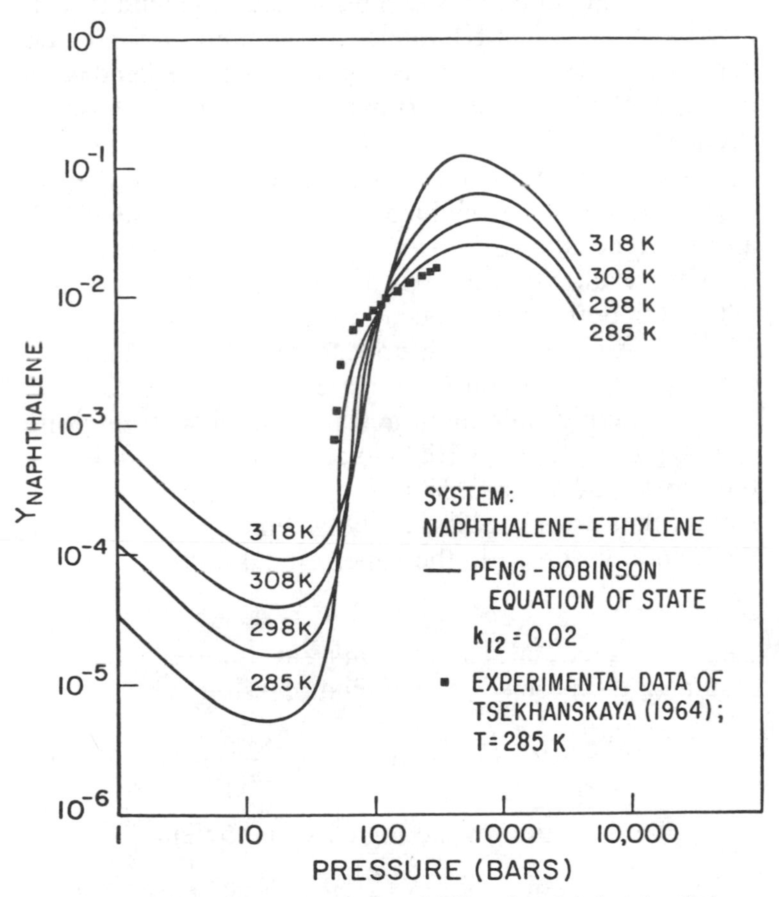

Figure 1.23—Effect of pressure on the solubility of naphthalene in ethylene.

function of pressure and covered a range up to about 1 kbar. Their smoothed data (as read from an enlargement of their original graphs) are plotted in Figure 1.24. At temperatures close to the upper critical end point (325.2 K), a maximum in concentration is clearly evident. At lower temperatures, the maximum is less obvious. The dashed curve in Figure 1.24 represents the results of calculating the concentration maximum from the Peng-Robinson equation of state. The simulation could be carried out only to 322 K; above this temperature, convergence becomes a problem as the second critical end point is approached, and the formation of two fluid phases is predicted.

Concentration maxima have also been noted by Czubryt et al. (1970) for the binary systems stearic acid-CO_2 and 1-octadecanol-CO_2. In these cases, the experimental data were all measured past the solubility maxima—which for both solutes occurred at a pressure of about 280 bar. An approximate correlation of their data was achieved by a solubility parameter model.

The solubility minimum and maximum with pressure can be related to the partial molal volume of the solute in the supercritical phase. With subscript 1 representing the solute, then with equilibrium between a pure solute and the solute dissolved in the supercritical fluid,

$$d\ln \hat{f}_1^F = d\ln \hat{f}_1^S \tag{1.11}$$

Expanding eq. (1.11) at constant temperature and assuming the pure solute is incompressible,

$$\frac{V_1^F}{RT}dP + \left(\frac{\partial \ln \hat{f}_1^F}{\partial \ln y_1}\right)_{T,P} d\ln y_1 = \frac{V_1^S}{RT}dP \tag{1.12}$$

Using the definition of the fugacity coefficient,

$$\phi_1^F = \hat{f}_1^F / y_1 P \tag{1.13}$$

then eq. (1.12) can be rearranged to give

$$\left(\frac{\partial \ln y_1}{\partial P}\right)_T = \frac{\left(\dfrac{V_1^S - \bar{V}_1^F}{RT}\right)}{\left[1 + \left(\dfrac{\partial \ln \phi_1}{\partial \ln y_1}\right)_{T,P}\right]} \tag{1.14}$$

ϕ_1 may be expressed in terms of y_1, T, and P with an equation of state, as shown in eq. (1.2). For naphthalene

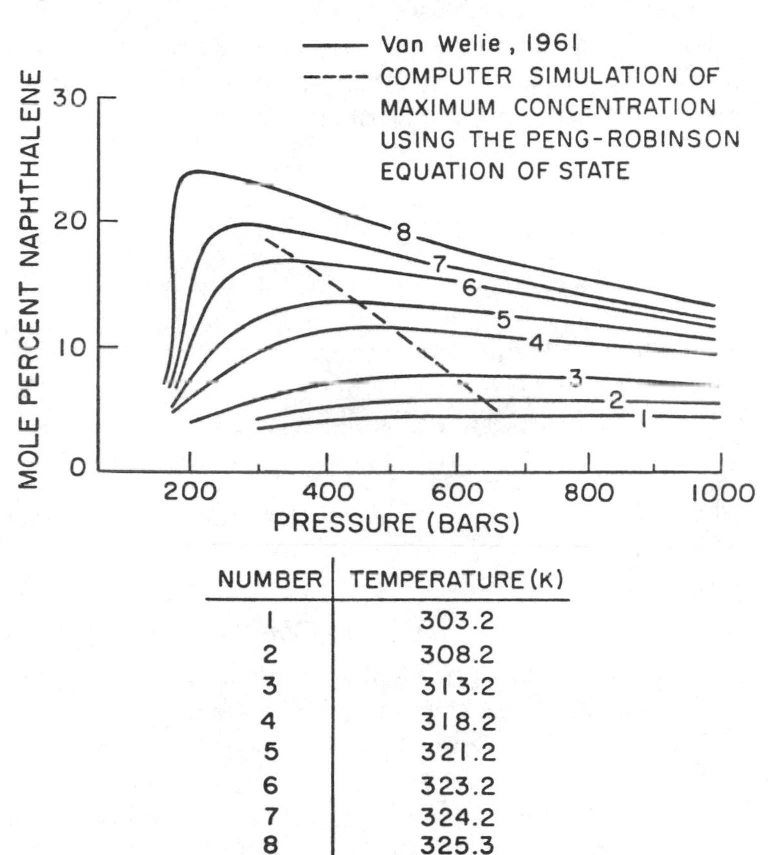

NUMBER	TEMPERATURE (K)
1	303.2
2	308.2
3	313.2
4	318.2
5	321.2
6	323.2
7	324.2
8	325.3

Figure 1.24—Maximum solubilities of naphthalene in ethylene. Van Welie and Diepen 1961.

as the solute in ethylene, $(\partial \ln\phi_1/\partial \ln y_1)_{T,P}$ was never less than −0.4 over a pressure range up to the 4 kbar limit studied. Thus the extreme in concentration occurs when $V_1^S = \bar{V}_1^F$.

Again using the Peng-Robinson equation of state, $\bar{V}^F$ was computed for naphthalene in ethylene as a function of pressure and temperature. The 318 K isotherm is shown in Figure 1.25. At low pressures, $\bar{V}^F$ is large and positive; it would approach an ideal gas molar volume as $P \rightarrow 0$. With an increase in pressure, $\bar{V}_1^F$ decreases and becomes equal to V_1^S; this then corresponds to the maximum in concentration described earlier.

Energy Effects

The extraction of a solute into a supercritical fluid under isothermal and isobaric conditions requires a heat interaction with the environment. It can be shown that for each mole of solute removal (N_1), the heat interaction (Q) may be expressed as

$$dQ/dN_1 = (\bar{H}_1 - H_1^S) \tag{1.15}$$

where $\bar{H}_1$ is the partial molar enthalpy in the supercritical phase and H_1^S is the molar enthalpy of the solid solute. The enthalpy difference is given by

$$\bar{H}_1 - H_1^S = -R[\partial \ln y_1/\partial(1/T)]_P\,[1 + (\partial \ln\phi_1/\partial \ln y_1)_{T,P}] \tag{1.16}$$

The terms on the right hand side of eq. (1.16) may be evaluated from the Peng-Robinson equation of state. Values for the system phenanthrene-CO_2 are given in Table 1.2.

At low pressures, $\bar{H}_1 - H_1^S$ is essentially equal to the enthalpy of sublimation for phenanthrene. At high pressures, $\bar{H}_1 - H_1^S$ is about twice the enthalpy of fusion, as the extraction is now into a dense fluid and perhaps is closer to a melting than a vaporization process.

In the intermediate pressure region, there exists a retrograde phenomenon, and during the process of solid → fluid, heat must be removed to maintain an isothermal system. Since the Gibbs energy change, at equilibrium, is zero, the molar entropy of the solute in the fluid phase is lower than in the crystalline solid! Since there is always a positive entropy change associated with the formation of

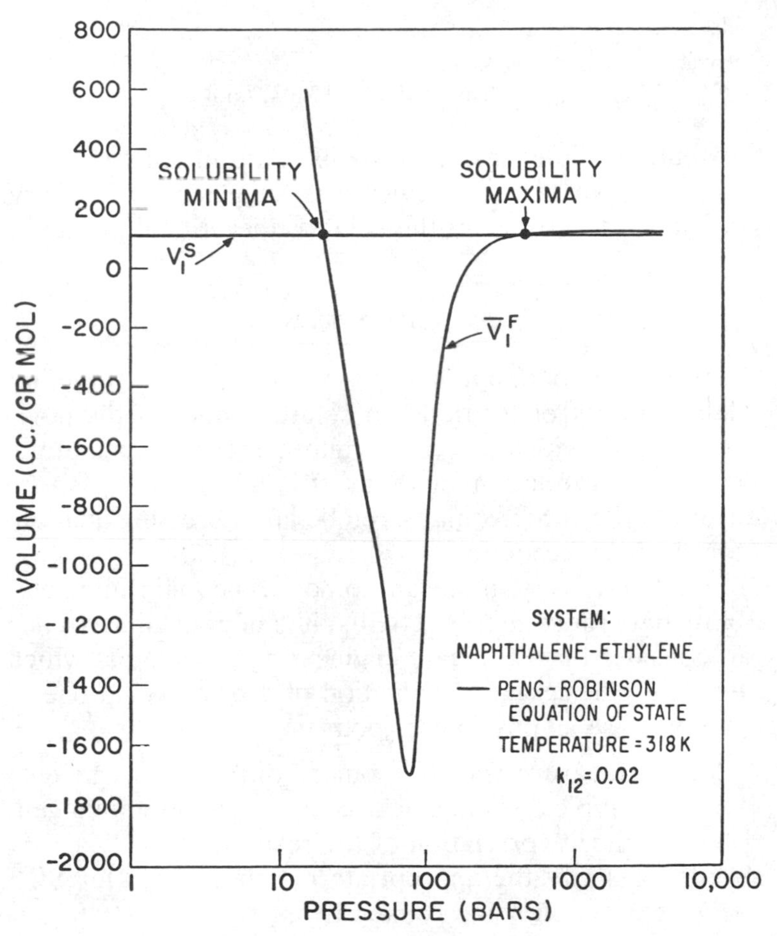

Figure 1.25—Partial molar volumes of naphthalene in ethylene.

Table 1.2. Differential Enthalpies of Solution for Phenanthrene-CO_2 at 328 K

P (bar)	$-R\left(\frac{\partial \ln y_1}{\partial(1/T)}\right)_P$ (kJ/mol)	$\left(\frac{\partial \ln \phi_1}{\partial \ln y_1}\right)_{T,P}$	$dQ/dN_1 = \bar{H}_1 - H_1^S$ (kJ/mol)
1	86.8	~0	86.8
10	83.3	~0	83.3
120	−46.4	−0.040	−48.3
300	28.7	−0.155	34.0

NOTE: $\Delta H_{fusion} = 18.7$ kJ/mol
$\Delta H_{sublimation}$ (at triple point) = 87.4 kJ/mol

a solution, the excess entropy of solution must be large and negative. This conclusion is suggestive of a very definite "structure" of the solute-supercritical phase.

Future Studies

We need to obtain additional equilibrium solubility data with a broader range of solutes (more of the polar type) with various solvents to allow further testing of the available correlation methods. Liquids should also be used. Perhaps SCFs may even be an interesting medium for chemical reactions.

While it is very important to possess equilibrium solubility data for solutes and SCFs, it is of equal importance to consider the significant engineering parameters which enter any design and evaluation of a proposed process. We propose as possible objectives:

(*a*) to measure selective binary diffusion coefficients for typical solutes in an SCF and to attempt a generalized correlation of the results;

(*b*) to clarify the appropriate j_m relationship for SCF extraction using packed beds;

(*c*) to simulate a transient packed bed SCF extraction to indicate quantitatively the relationships between the key dimensionless groups and to generalize the effect of different variables on the extraction.

Each of these three objectives is discussed below.

BINARY DIFFUSION COEFFICIENTS IN SCFS

Few experimental data are available for D_{AB} in the high pressure region. Reid and associates (1977) reviewed many of the available experimental studies and concluded that a general correlation is not yet possible. They point out that the product of $D_{AB} \times \rho$ often decreases at high pressures, and the composition of the gas (fluid) phase may be important. Tee et al. (1966) show $D_{AB}\rho$ for several simple systems as a function of reduced pressure and temperature. Slight decreases in $D_{AB}\rho$ were noted, but in no cases were the systems near their critical points. Self-diffusivities were correlated by Slattery (1955) as $D_{AA}\rho = f(P_r,T_r)$. The generalized chart has been published in Bird et al. (1960). This plot suggests that D_{AA} can become very small in the critical region.

More pertinent to the SCF study where solutes are often rather complex molecules, Tsekhanskaya (1971) measured the diffusion coefficient of naphthalene in supercritical CO_2 in the region near the first critical end point (307.7 K, ρ = 467 kg/m^3, y (naphthalene) 3×10^{-3}). Measurements were made by noting the mass changes of a naphthalene tablet in a diffusion cell. The SCF density was varied from 250 kg/m^3 to 592 kg/m^3 at 308.2 K. (This corresponds to a pressure change of only 73.5–83.5 bar.) The results are shown in Table 1.3.

Clearly ρD_{AB} is not constant in this region, and the value of D_{AB} becomes very small near the first critica'

Table 1.3. Diffusion Coefficients in Supercritical CO_2

T = 308.2 K				
P (bar)	ρ (kg/m^3)	ρ (mole/m^3)	D (m^2/s)	ρD (mole/m s)
73.5	250	5,680	4.8×10^{-9}	2.7×10^{-5}
78.3	350	7,960	1.4×10^{-9}	1.1×10^{-5}
80.2	460	10,450	6×10^{-11}	6×10^{-7}
82.1	560	12,720	3.6×10^{-9}	4.6×10^{-5}
83.5	592	13,460	6.9×10^{-9}	9.3×10^{-5}

NOTE: For reference, the critical properties of CO_2 are T_c = 304.2 K, P_c = 73.8 bar, and ρ_c = 10,600 mole/m^3.

end point. Others have suggested a similar behavior for D_{AB} in the vicinity of a consolute point for liquid-liquid systems (see Tsekhanskaya 1968 for data and many references).

Further experiments were reported for the diffusion coefficient of naphthalene in CO_2 by Vinkler and Morozov (1975). Only one isotherm was studied above the critical temperature of CO_2 (304 K), and no pressures exceeded the critical pressure of CO_2 (73.8 bar). At 313 K, values of D_{AB} varied from 7.9×10^{-7}m^2/s at 6.0 bar, to 7.5×10^{-8}m^2/s at 45 bar. Other experiments were made by Iomtev and Tsekhanskaya (1964) with both naphthalene-ethylene and naphthalene-CO_2 systems in the SCF phase. There is reported a strong pressure dependence on D_{AB}, but temperature variations have a surprisingly small effect. The product $D_{AB}\rho$ decreased with pressure. These data were taken in a static diffusion cell, and this method is believed to be less accurate than the dynamic procedure used later by Vinker and Morozov (1975). Also their values do not agree well with those of Tsekhanskaya (1971) in the region of overlap.

Rance and Cussler (1974) studied iodine dissolution rates in supercritical CO_2 from 293 to 348 K and at pressures up to about 300 bar (at 348 K). No diffusion coefficients were determined, but the iodine flux rate was shown to increase strongly with both temperature and density (or pressure) in the SCF range. They ascribe these changes to the enhancement of solubility in the SCF region more than to variations in transport properties (e.g., D_{AB}) or j_m. (D_{AB} was assumed to be inversely proportional to density.) This measured effect of pressure on flux rates appears reasonable, but the increase in flux rate with temperature at constant pressure would suggest that there was no retrograde solubility region. As such regions have been noted for most CO_2-solute systems (see previous section), it would be most interesting to study I_2 solubility in CO_2 to verify this anomaly.

Rance and Cussler also noted that the I_2 flux became very small in the vicinity of the CO_2 critical point.

Completing this brief survey, Bartman and Schneider (1973) studied the use of supercritical CO_2 in chromatography but reported no specific diffusion coefficients. Schneider (1978) shows some data for D_{AB} for benzene-CO_2 at 40° C up to about 150 bar but gives no compositions.

In summary, very few experimental data now exist for binary diffusion coefficients in the SCF region of interest for extraction studies, and we suggest that experiments be conducted to obtain such information.

j_m RELATIONSHIPS FOR SCF EXTRACTION

As most SCF extraction operations proposed to date used a *packed column* extractor, the discussion in this section is related to this case.

Treybal (1963) provides a summary of j_m relationships to use for packed beds. Two distinctions are made—i.e., between liquids (large Schmidt numbers) and gases (low Schmidt numbers). Correlations in the two groups are quite different. SCFs have Schmidt numbers which are intermediate in value between liquids and gases, as shown in Table 1.4. While the properties shown in this table are only approximate, they do illustrate the dilemma in selecting an appropriate correction to estimate j_m factors for packed beds in contact with SCFs.

Table 1.4. Ranges of Transport Properties

	Water solvent at ambient conditions	Air solvent at low pressure	SCF*
$\nu (m^2/s)$	10^{-6}	10^{-5}	10^{-7}
$D_{AB} (m^2/s)$	$\sim 10^{-9}$	$\sim 10^{-4}$	$\sim 10^{-8}$
Sc	$\sim 10^3$	$\sim 10^{-1}$	~ 10

*E.g., CO_2-naphthalene at $T > T_{c_{CO_2}}$, $P > P_{c_{CO_2}}$.

Storck and Coeuret (1980) recently reviewed existing packed bed correlations for j_m when liquids are used as solvents. Their results can be rearranged to give

$$\epsilon \, j_m = 0.2 \left[\frac{4.5(1-\epsilon)^2}{Re^2} + \frac{0.3(1-\epsilon)}{Re} \right]^{1/3} \qquad (1.17)$$

where $j_m = (k/u)(Sc)^{2/3}$
ϵ = void volume
u = superficial velocity
k = mass transfer coefficient
Re = Reynolds' number = $u/\nu a$
ν = kinematic viscosity
a = area of solute / volume of bed
Sc = Schmidt number

At low Re, the first term is dominant, and the resulting simplification agrees well with the correlation proposed earlier by Wilson and Geankopolis (1966) for $0.0016 < Re < 55$.

The Re range one would expect to be used for SCF extraction is $10 < Re < 10^3$, so the transition region for

$j_m = f(Re)$ would also be involved. At high Re, j_m would vary as $Re^{-1/3}$ by the equation above (Wilson and Geankopolis suggest the exponent to be -0.31).

For gases, Wilson and Geankopolis recommend the correlation by Gupta and Thodos (1962)

$$\epsilon j_m = 10^{-2} + 0.863(Re^{0.58} - 0.483)^{-1}$$

which predicts significantly higher j_m values than the liquid correlations, especially at low Re. Bradshaw and Bennett (1961) also state that gases have a higher j_m than liquids at the same Re.

Since SCF extraction involves Sc number values intermediate between liquids and gases, it is not clear how to choose the appropriate correlation for $k = f(u, Re, Sc, \epsilon)$. We suggest that mass transfer coefficients be obtained experimentally in a packed bed of solute contacted by an SCF, and the results correlated as a function of the variables noted above.

SIMULATION OF A PACKED BED SCF EXTRACTOR

Illustrative of what one might hope to accomplish in this objective, consider the problem of estimating the quantity of solute extracted in a single packed bed of a solid feed material. We assume that this feed contains, initially, some given concentration of an extractable solute. The solute need not be homogeneously distributed, but the initial concentration profile of the solute in the feed solid is assumed to be known.

The bed is contacted with an SCF entering at a known concentration of solute. (The inlet solute concentration is determined by the clean-up efficiency in an external recycle loop.) Flow in the extractor may be assumed to be plug-flow (but some axial mixing could be allowed depending upon the flow conditions). Solute is extracted and removed externally in the recycle loop. After a given period of time, one would like to know the *average* solute concentration remaining in the feed material.

Many variables could affect this process, e.g., temperature, pressure, solvent flow rate, the partition coefficient for the system, the bed geometry, etc. It is very difficult to estimate the effects of changes in such variables on the percentage extracted versus time. For example, if the temperature alone were to be increased, the diffusion coefficients of the solute in the solid (and in the SCF) would rise. But, depending on the absolute level of the temperature and pressure, the partition coefficient could either increase or decrease. To some extent, the mass transfer coefficient would also change.

It would therefore be of real value to have the ability to simulate the extraction process to allow an optimal design in terms of the independent process variables. Any simulation of the extraction would have to consider a number of rate and equilibrium steps.

1. The solute in the solid will move to the interface by a diffusional process, and within each particle, a concentration gradient will be established. We could assume all particles at the same axial location will be identical, but solid concentration profiles will vary with axial location. The solute diffusivity (as affected by temperature and, perhaps, by solute concentration), the particle size and shape, and bed geometry are important variables.
2. At the solid-SCF interface, local equilibrium exists and is related to a partition coefficient, K. This coefficient is a function of temperature, pressure, and possibly solute concentration in the solid.
3. Solute is transferred to the SCF by a mass transfer mechanism which we can assume to be specified in terms of a mass transfer coefficient and a driving force between the interface and bulk SCF. Flow

rates and physical properties of the SCF and solute would affect the mass transfer coefficient, while T and P would be the principal variables controlling the driving force for solute transfer.

4. The SCF changes in solute concentration (and perhaps in T, P, velocity) over the axial length of the bed. This variation would have to be taken into account.

We outline a preliminary analysis below. For simplicity, we let the solid particles be spheres with a radius R. The solute concentration in any sphere is C' and would be a function of radial position r, and implicitly, of time and axial location. If we define

$$\mu = rC'(r) \tag{1.18}$$

then the diffusion equation within any single solid particle can be written as

$$\partial\mu/\partial t = D'\partial^2\mu/\partial r^2 \tag{1.19}$$
$$o < r < R$$

where D' is the diffusion coefficient of the solute within the solid sphere (assumed constant). We note also the conditions,

$$\mu = 0, \ r = o \tag{1.20}$$

$$\mu_o(r) = rC'_o(r), \ t = o \tag{1.21}$$

At the solid-SCF interface

$$k(KC' - C'') = -D'(\partial C'/\partial r) \tag{1.22}$$

where k is the mass transfer coefficient in the SCF phase, K is the partition coefficient, and C'' is the solute concentration in the bulk SCF.

In the SCF, by continuity,

$$u\frac{\partial C''}{\partial x} + \frac{\epsilon\partial C''}{\partial t} + (1-\epsilon)\frac{\partial C'}{\partial t} = 0 \tag{1.23}$$

In eq. (1.23), ϵ is the void fraction, x is the length variable measured axially from the inlet, and u is the superficial velocity.

The inlet solute concentration in the SCF is

$$C''(t) = C_o''(t), \ x = 0 \tag{1.24}$$

The ultimate objective is to determine the bed-averaged solute concentration $\bar{C}'$ at after a given period of extraction. If V_b is the bed volume occupied by solid, then

$$\bar{\bar{C}}' = (\int \bar{C}' dV)/V \tag{1.25}$$

with

$$\bar{C}' = (3/R^3) \int_o^R r\mu \ dr \tag{1.26}$$

That is, $\bar{C}'$ is the average solute concentration at some axial location at time t.

From $\bar{\bar{C}}'$, one can obtain the percentage removal of solute in the bed.

There are a number of ways to nondimensionalize these equations to allow numerical solution. We suggest one method below as our preliminary calculations employed it. The principal dimensionless groups were found to be

$$\text{dimensionless time: } \tau = D' t/R^2 \tag{1.27}$$

$$\text{dimensionless flow: } F = \mu t K/L(1-\epsilon) \tag{1.28}$$

(L is the bed length)

$$\text{dimensional Biot number: } M = kKR/D' \tag{1.29}$$

Another group involving the void fractions and bed dimensions may be specified, but it is usually so nearly a constant that it will not be considered here.

The equations given above can be solved to obtain generalized curves to relate τ, F, and M for given values of $\bar{\bar{C}}'$. These curves could then be used to evaluate variations in T, P, flow rate, solid particle size, bed porosity, etc., on the solute removal at given times. The correlations obtained would be very useful not only for SCF extraction but in many solid-fluid leaching processes.

We also note that values of D' must be available. These would have to be obtained by separate experiments. For example, in green coffee beans, Bichsel and associates (1976) have measured diffusion coefficients of caffeine under a variety of conditions.

We note that SCF extraction of solutes differs in one very important way from normal extraction—that is, the solvent is normally a *poor* solvent. Or, in other words, the partition coefficient K is very small. In normal extraction processes, a good solvent is chosen (large K) to minimize process volumes and flow rates. In SCF extraction, solute concentrations in the solvent are usually very small, and this important fact may lead to significant external mass transfer limitations. The concept is not unlike that of extracting an adjuvant from a polymer with a poor solvent. As has been shown in such cases, the mass transfer rates in the solvent may play a very important role even for cases where the adjuvant diffusion coefficient in the polymer is very low (Reid et al. 1980).

Extending this concept, the simulation could also cover a series of extraction vessels through which an SCF was circulated in a counter-current manner. The vessels containing solids would be added and removed at discrete time intervals to simulate an actual process.

As another area of interest in future SCF studies, we note that almost always, pure SCFs have been used. Yet there is evidence, summarized below, which would suggest that a significant enhancement in the solvent power of an SCF may be achieved by the addition of small amounts of a second component. Thus we propose as possible research objectives:

(*a*) To measure experimentally the equilibrium solubility of a number of diverse solids in a pure SCF *and* in the same SCF modified by the addition of small concentrations of an appropriate second component.

(*b*) To use the data obtained in (*a*) to develop correlations and, hopefully, predictor techniques to allow an assessment of this scheme to enhance solubilities in industrially important processes.

In a British patent (Studiengesellschaft Kohle, M.B.H., 1967), the statement is made (relative to SCF uses): "An impressive example is the removal of chlorophyll from commercial plant parts by means of a supercritical gas to which organic compounds of higher volatility have been added." No data were given. The concept of adding second components was given the name "entrainer" and was noted by Panzer and associates (1978). They stated: "A preliminary study of the separations of glyceride mixtures using supercritical carbon dioxide as a solvent has been made. Little separation was achieved using pure carbon dioxide but considerable improvements resulted by the addition of *entrainers* carbon tetrachloride and *n*-hexane." In this case, the concentrations of carbon tetrachloride or *n*-hexane were not small (30–40 weight percent). The authors suggest using acetone as an entrainer for the same system. (But *n*-hexane and acetone had different selectivities in a mixed-glyceride system.) Peter and Brunner (1978) describe the use of acetone entrainers in supercritical propane to separate monoglycerides from oleic glycerides. Brunner (1980) noted that entrainers could significantly change the retrograde temperature region. In none of these papers or presentations was there any attempt made to quantify or clarify the behavior of these second-components.

We too have seen this second-component effect. In the first instance, we were making exploratory runs with some natural alkaloids to determine in an approximate fashion their solubility in supercritical CO_2. In one case we added less than 1 mole percent water and found an enhancement in solubility which ranged from 10 to 50%. Also, as noted earlier, when we studied binary solid mixtures, we noted that solubilities could be significantly affected by small variations in the fluid-phase composition. Here, we had effectively introduced an entrainer by using a solid mixture.

Very little is known about how entrainers affect composition—or, more importantly, how one could select an entrainer to obtain higher solubilities or better selectivities.

Acknowledgments

Over the past several years, I have enjoyed the association with Ronald Kurnik during his doctorate studies in supercritical extraction. Many of the experimental data presented in this paper were obtained by him during his research. I am also indebted to Alain Besson for many of the ideas in modelling solid beds.

The research was carried out at M.I.T. and was jointly supported by Nestle, Inc., and the National Science Foundation.

Literature Cited

Adams, R. M., Alfred H. Knebel, and Donald E. Rhodes. 1978. "Critical Solvent Deashing of Liquefied Coal." Paper presented at 71st AIChE meeting, Nov. 15, Miami.

Andrews, T. 1887. "On the Properties of Matter in the Gaseous and Liquid States under Various Conditions," *Phil. Trans. Roy. Soc. London 178*, 45.

Balder, J. R., and J. M. Prausnitz. 1966. "Thermodynamics of

Ternary Liquid-Supercritical Gas Systems with Applications for High Pressure Vapor Extraction." *Ind. Eng. Chem. Fund. 5*, 449.

Bartle, K. P., T. G. Martin, and D. F. Williams. 1975. "Chemical Nature of a Supercritical Gas Extract of Coal at 350° C." *Fuel 54*, 226.

Bartmann, D., and G. M. Schneider. 1973. "Experimental Results and Physico-Chemical Aspects of Supercritical Chromatography with Carbon Dioxide as the Mobile Phase." *J. Chromat. 83*, 135.

Barton, P., and M. R. Fenske. 1970. "Hydrocarbon Extraction of Saline Waters," *Ind. Eng. Chem. Proc. res. Dev. 9*, 18.

Baughman, G. L., S. P. Westhoff, S. Dincer, D. D. Duston, and A. J. Kidnay. 1975. "The Solid and Vapor Phase Equilibrium and Interaction Second Virial Coefficients for Argon +, Nitrogen +, Methane +, and Helium + Neopentane, II: Analysis of Results." *J. Chem. Thermo 7*, 875.

Bichsel, B., S. Gál, and R. Signer. 1976. "Diffusion Phenomena During Decaffeination of Coffee Beans." *J. Fd. Technol. 11*, 637.

Bird, R. B., W. E. Stewart, and E. N. Lightfoot. 1960. *Transport Phenomena.* John Wiley and Sons, New York.

Bradshaw, R. D., and G. D. Bennett. 1961. "Fluid Particle Mass Transfer in a Packed Bed," *AIChE J. 7*, 48.

Brunner, G. 1980. Discussion at the Supercritical Fluid Extraction Symposium Electrochemical Meeting, May 14–15, St. Louis, Mo.

Czubryt, J. J., M. N. Myers, and J. C. Giddings. 1970. "Solubility Phenomena in Dense Carbon Dioxide Gas in the Range 270 to 1900 Atmospheres." *J. Phys. Chem. 74*, 4260.

Diepen, G.A.M. and F.E.C. Scheffer. 1948*a*. "On Critical Phenomena of Saturated Solutions in Binary Systems." *J. Am. Chem. Soc. 70*, 4081.

Diepen, G.A.M., and F.E.C. Scheffer. 1948*b*. "The Solubility of Naphthalene in Supercritical Ethylene." *J. Am. Chem. Soc. 70*, 4085.

Diepen, G.A.M., and F.E.C. Scheffer. 1953. "The Solubility of Naphthalene in Supercritical Ethylene: II." *J. Phys. Chem. 57*, 575.

Dokoupel, Z., G. van Soest, and M.D.P. Swenker. 1955. "On the Equilibrium between the Solid Phase and the Gas Phase of the Systems Hydrogen-Nitrogen, Hydrogen-Carbon Monoxide, and Hydrogen-Nitrogen-Carbon Monoxide." *App. Sci. Res. A5*, 182.

Eisenbeiss, J. 1964. "A Basic Study of the Solubility of Solids in Gases at High Pressures." Final Report, Contract No. DA 18-108-AMC-244(A), Southwest Research Institute, August, San Antonio.

Elgin, J. C., and J. J. Weinstock. 1959. "Phase Equilibrium Molecular Transport Thermodynamics." *J. Chem. Eng. Data 4*, 3.

Ewald, A. H. 1955. "The Solubility of Solids in Gases, Part III: The Solubility of Solid Xenon and Carbon Dioxide." *Trans. Far. Soc. 51*, 347.

Ewald, A. H., W. B. Jepson, and J. S. Rowlinson. 1953. "The Solubility of Solids in Gases." *Disc. Far. Soc. A5*, 238.

Gangoli, N., and G. Thodos. 1977. "Liquid Fuels and Chemical Feedstocks from Coal by Supercritical Gas Extraction." *Ind. Eng. Chem. Prod. Res. Dev. 16*, 208.

Gratch, S. 1945–46. "Low-Temperature Properties of CO_2-Air-Mixtures by Means of a One-Stage Experiment." Proj G-9A, Univ. of Penn. Thermodynamics Research Laboratory.

Gupta, A. S., and G. Thodos. 1962. "Mass and Heat Transfer in the Flow of Fluids through Fixed and Fluidized Beds of Spherical Particles," *AIChE J. 8*, 608.

Hag A.G. 1973*a*. "Method of Producing Caffeine-Free Black Tea." Br. 1 333 362.

Hag A.G. 1973*b*. "Method of Producing Spice Extracts with a Natural Composition." Br. 1 336 511.

Hag A.G. 1974*a*. "Method of Extracting Nicotine from Tobacco." Br. 1 357 645.

Hag A.G. 1974*b*. "Method of Producing Caffeine-Free Coffee Extract." Br. 1 346 134.

Hag A.G. 1974*c*. "Method of Producing Cocoa Butter." Br. 1 356 750.

Hag A.G. 1974*d*. "Method of Producing Vegetable Fats and Oils." Br. 1 356 749.

Hag A.G. 1975. "Method of Producing Hop Extracts." Br. 1 388 581.

Hannay, J. B., and J. Hogarth. 1879. "On the Solubility of Solids in Gases." *Proc. Roy. Soc.* (London) *29*, 324.

Hannay, J. B., and J. Hogarth. 1880. "On the Solubility of Solids in Gases." *Proc. Roy. Soc.* (London) *30*, 178.

Hinckley, R. B., and R. C. Reid. 1964. "Rapid Estimation of Minimum Solubility of Solids in Gases." *AIChE J. 10*, 416.

Hiza, M. J., and A. J. Kidnay. 1966. "Solid-Vapor Equilibrium in the System Neon-Methane." *Cryogenics 6*, 348.

Hiza, M. J., C. K. Heck, and A. J. Kidnay. 1968. "Liquid-Vapor and Solid-Vapor Equilibrium in the System Hydrogen-Ethylene." *Chem. Eng. Prog. Symp. Ser. 64*, no. 88, 57.

Holder, C. H., and O. Maass. 1940. "Solubility Measurements in the Region of the Critical Point." *Can. J. Res. 188*, 293.

Holm, L. W. 1975. "Carbon Dioxide Flooding for Increased Oil Recovery." *AIME Petro. Trans. 216*, 225.

Hubert, P., and O. Vitzhum. 1978. "Fluid Extraction of Hops, Spices, and Tobacco with Supercritical Gases." *Angew. Chem. Int. Ed. Engl. 17*, 710.

Iomtev, M. B., and Y. V. Tsekhanskaya. 1964. "Diffusion of Naphthalene in Compressed Ethylene and Carbon Dioxide." *Russ. J. Phys. Chem. 38*, 485.

Irani, C. A., and E. W. Funk. 1977. "Separations Using Supercritical Gases." In *CRC Handbook: Recent Developments in Separation Science*. CRC Press, Boca Raton, Fl.

Jentoft, R. E., and T. H. Gouw. 1972. "Apparatus for Supercritical Fluid Chromatography with Carbon Dioxide as the Mobile Phase," *Anal. Chem. 44*, 681.

Johnston, K. P., and C. A. Eckert. 1981. "An Analytical Carnahan-Starling-van der Waals Model for Solubility of Hydrocarbon Solids in Supercritical Fluids." *AIChE J. 27*, 773.

Jones, D., and R. Staehle. 1973. "High-Temperature Electrochemistry in Aqueous Solutions." Central Electricity Research Laboratory, National Society of Corrosion Engineers, p. 131.

Kennedy, G. C. 1944. "The Hydrothermal Solubility of Silica." *Economic Geology 39*, 25.

Kennedy, G. C. 1950. "A Portion of the System Silica-Water." *Economic Geology 45*, 629.

King, A. D., and W. W. Robertson. 1962. "Solubility of Naphthalene in Compressed Gases." *J. Chem. Phys. 37*, 1453.

Klesper, E. 1978. "Chromatography with Supercritical Fluids." *Angew. Chem. Int. Ed. Engl. 17*, 738.

Knebel, A. H., and D. E. Rhodes. 1978. "Critical Solvent Deashing of Liquefied Coal." Paper presented at the 13th Intersociety Energy Conversion Engineering Conference, Aug. 20–25, San Diego.

Krukonis, V. 1980. Private communication.

McHugh, M., and M. Paulaitis. 1980. "Solid Solubilities of Naphthalene and Biphenyl in Supercritical Carbon Dioxide." *J. Chem. Eng. Data 25*, 326.

McKinley, C., J. Brewer, and E.S.J. Wang. 1962. "Solid-Vapor Equilibria of the Oxygen-Hydrogen System." *Adv. Cry. Eng. 7*, 114.

Modell, M., R. P. de Fillippi, and V. Krukonis. 1978. "Regeneration of Activated Carbon with Supercritical Carbon Dioxide." Paper presented at ACS meeting, Sept. 14, Miami.

Modell, M., R. Robey, V. Krukonis, R. de Fillippi, and D. Oestreich. 1979. "Supercritical Fluid Regeneration of Activated Carbon." Paper presented at 87th AIChE National Meeting, Boston.

Morey, G. W. 1957. "The Solubility of Solids in Gases." *Economic Geology 52*, 227.

Najour, G. C., and A. D. King, Jr. 1966. "Solubility of Naphthalene in Compressed Methane, Ethylene, and Carbon Dioxide." *J. Chem. Phys. 45*, 1915.

Najour, G. C., and A. D. King, Jr. 1970. "Solubility of Anthracene in Compressed Methane, Ethylene, Ethane, and Carbon Dioxide: The Correlation of Anthracene-Gas Second Virial Coefficients using Pseudo Critical Parameters." *J. Chem. Phys. 52*, 5206.

Newsham, D.M.T., and O. P. Stigset. 1978. "Separation Processes Involving Supercritical Gases." *I. Chem. E. Symp. Ser.*, no. 54, p. 1.

Panzer, F., S.R.M. Ellis, and T. R. Bott. 1978. "Separation of Glycerides in the Presence of Supercritical Carbon Dioxide." *I. Chem. E. Ser.*, no. 54, p. 165.

Paul, P.F.M., and W. S. Wise. 1971. *The Principles of Gas Extraction*. Mills and Boon, London, Monograph CE/S.

Peng, D. Y., and D. B. Robinson. 1976. "A New Two Constant Equation of State." *Ind. Eng. Chem. Fund. 15*, 59.

Peter, S., G. Brunner, and R. Riha. 1974. "Phasengleichgewichte bei hohen Drücken und Möglichkeiten ihrer technischen Anwendung." *Chem. Ing. Tech. 46*, 623.

Peter, S., and G. Brunner. 1978. "The Separation of Nonvolatile Substances by Means of Compressed Gases in Countercurrent Processes." *Angew. Chem. Int. Ed. Engl. 17*, 746.

Prausnitz, J. M. 1969. *Molecular Thermodynamics of Fluid Phase Equilibria*. Prentice-Hall, Englewood Cliffs, N.J.

Rance, R. W., and E. L. Cussler. 1974. "Fast Fluxes with Supercritical Solvents." *AIChE J. 20*, 353.

Redlich, O., and J.N.S. Kwong. 1949. "On the Thermodynamics of Solutions. V. An Equation of State. Fugacities of Gaseous Solutions," *Chem. Rev. 44*, 233.

Reid, R. C., J. M. Prausnitz, and T. K. Sherwood. 1977. *The Properties of Gases and Liquids*. McGraw Hill, New York.

Reid, R. C., K. R. Sidman, A. D. Schwope, and D. E. Till. 1980. "The Loss of Adjuvants from Polymer Films to Foods or Food Simulants: The Effect of the External Phase," *Ind. Eng. Chem. Prod. Res. Develop. 19*, 580.

Rowlinson, J. S., and M. J. Richardson. 1959. "Solubility of Solids in Compressed Gases." *Adv. Chem. Phys. II*, 85.

Sax, N. I. 1979. *Dangerous Properties of Industrial Materials*. 5th ed. Van Nostrand Reinhold, New York, p. 718.

Schneider, G. M. 1978. "Physiochemical Principles of Extraction with Supercritical Gases." *Angew. Chem. Int. Ed. Engl. 17*, 716.

Sie, S. T., W. Van Beersum, and G.W.A. Rijnders. 1966. "High-Pressure Gas Chromatography with Supercritical

Fluids, I: The Effect of Pressure on Partition Coefficients in Gas-Liquid Chromatography with Carbon Dioxide as a Carrier Gas." *Sep. Sci. 1*, 459.

Slattery, J. C. 1955. "Diffusion Coefficients and the Principle of Corresponding States," M.S. thesis, Univ. of Wisconsin, Madison.

Snedeker, R. A. 1955. "Phase Equilibria in Systems with Supercritical Carbon Dioxide." Ph.D. thesis, Princeton Univ.

Sonntag, R. E., and G. J. Van Wylen. 1962. "The Solid-Vapor Equilibrium of Carbon Dioxide-Nitrogen." *Adv. Cry. Eng. 7*, 99.

Storck, A., and F. Coeuret. 1980. "Mass Transfer between a Flowing Liquid and a Wall or an Immersed Surface in Fixed Fluidized Beds." *Chem. Eng. J. 20*, 149.

Studiengesellschaft Kohle, M.B.H. 1967. Br. 1 057 911.

Tee, L. S., G. F. Kuether, R. C. Robinson, and W. E. Stewart. 1966. "Diffusion and Principles of Corresponding States." Paper presented at ADI Meeting, Div. of Refining, Houston.

Texaco. 1967. U.S. 3 318 805.

Treybal, R. E. 1963. *Mass Transfer Operations*. McGraw-Hill, New York.

Tsekhanskaya, Y. V. 1968. "Diffusion in the System p-Nitrophenol-Water in the Critical Region," *Russ. J. Phys. Chem. 49* (9), 1405.

Tsekhanskaya, Y. V. 1971. "Diffusion of Naphthalene in CO_2 Near Liquid-Gas Critical Point," *Russ. J. Phys. Chem. 42* (4), 532.

Tsekhanskaya, Y. V., M. B. Iomtev, and E. V. Mushkina. 1962. "Solubility of Diphenylamine and Naphthalene in Carbon Dioxide under Pressure." *Russ. J. Phys. Chem. 36*, 1177.

Tsekhanskaya, Y. V., M. B. Iomtev, and E. V. Mushkina. 1964. "Solubility of Naphthalene in Ethylene and Carbon Dioxide under Pressure." *Zh. Fiz. Khim. 38*, 2166.

Van Gunst, C. A. 1950. "De Oplosbaarheid Van Mengsels Van Vaste Stoffen in Superkritische Gassen." Diss. Univ. of Delft.

Van Leer, R. A., and M. Paulaitis. 1980. "Solubilities of Phe-

nol and Chlorinated Phenols in Supercritical Carbon Dioxide." *J. Chem. Eng. Data 25*, 257.
Van Nieuwenburg, C. J., and P. M. Van Zon. 1935. "Semi-Quantitative Measurement of the Solubility of Quartz in Steam." *Rec. Trav. Chim. 54*, 129.
Van Wasen, U., I. Swaid, and G. M. Schneider. 1980. "Physicochemical Principles and Applications of Supercritical Fluid Chromatography." *Angew. Chem. Int. Ed. Engl. 19*, 575.
Van Welie, G.S.A., and G.A.M. Diepen. 1961. "The *P-T-x* Space Model of the System Ethylene-Naphthalene." *J. Rec. Trav. Chim. 80*, 659.
Vinkler, E. G. and V. S. Morozov. 1975. "Measurement of Diffusion Coefficients of Vapours of Solids in Compressed Gases. II. Diffusion Coefficients of Naphthalene in Nitrogen and Carbon Dioxide," *Russ. J. Phys. Chem. 49* (9), 1405.
Vitzthum, O., and P. Hubert. 1975. Ger. 2 357 590.
Waldeck, W., G. Lynn, and A. Hill. 1932. "Aqueous Solubility of Salts at High Temperature, II: The Ternary System Na_2CO_3-$NaHCO_3$-H_2O from 100–200°." *J. Am. Chem. Soc. 56*, 43.
Webster, T. J. 1950. "The Effect on Water Vapor Pressure of Superimposed Air Pressure." *J. Chem. Soc.* (London) *69*, 343.
Wilke, G. 1978. "Extraction with Supercritical Gases." *Angew. Chem. Int. Ed. Engl. 17*, 701.
Wilson, E. J., and C. J. Geankopolis. 1966. "Liquid and Mass Transfer at Very Low Reynolds Numbers in Packed Beds," *Ind. Eng. Chem. Fundam. 5*, 9.
Wise, W. S. 1970. "Solvent Extraction of Coal." *Chem. Ind.* (London), 950.
Zellner, M. G., C. J. Sterner, L. C. Claitor, and J. M. Geist. 1962. "Vapor Phase Solubility of Oxygen in Helium at Low Temperatures and Pressures up to 6500 psi." Paper presented at AIChE meeting, August, Denver.
Zhuze, T. P. 1960. "Compressed Hydrocarbon Gases as a Solvent." *Petroleum* (London) *23*, 298.
Zosel, K. 1978. "Separation with Supercritical Gases: Practical Applications." *Angew. Chem. Int. Ed. Engl. 17*, 702.

2

Migration of Oligomers and Additives from Plastics to Foods

I. The Problem and the Problems

As viewed by the consumer, the packaging and marketing of food have undergone dramatic changes during the twentieth century. Bulk containers have been almost completely replaced, first by traditional materials such as glass, metal, paper, and cardboard, and more recently by a variety of plastic wraps, bags, jars, and boxes. Appropriate selection of the plastic retards detrimental changes, such as oxidation or flavor loss. Recently, asceptic packaging systems have been developed, and fresh milk, for example, may be stored at room temperature for extended periods of time.

Yet, with the enhanced use of plastic food wraps, there is concern that components of the plastic (low-molecular-weight oligomers and additives) may migrate into the food. These would then appear as indirect food additives. Direct food additives (materials such as emulsifiers and antioxidants intentionally added to the natural food) have received the attention of governmental regulatory agencies for many years. France produced a list of approved additives in 1912 (Haesen and Schwartze 1979). Indirect food additives from plastic wraps and containers are also of concern to these same regulatory bodies.

To determine whether or not a given plastic wrap / food combination is safe from a consumer's point of view is the problem. It is a difficult one. The extent of any migration depends upon a number of variables, such as the type of polymer and migrating species, the food, the temperature and time of contact, the concentration of migrant in the polymer, and so on. The role of many of these has, in fact, not been clearly delineated.

Only over the last ten years have serious attempts been made to understand the migration process, and most of the experimental work has been carried out by either Unilever in Germany or PIRA in Great Britain. Recent contracts by the U.S. Food and Drug Administration (FDA) have, however, intensified the level of activity in the United States. A survey of many of the analytical models now available is given later in section III, and a comparison of a few experimental data with these models is presented in section IV.

While our data base is expanding rapidly, the job of a regulatory agency to certify a given polymer (with or without polymer adjuvants) as safe for a given food use is most difficult. There are many problems. In Section II, I describe briefly how the FDA operates in making decisions. The key element in any such evaluation is to select what is termed a food simulant or food simulating solvent. The introduction of this concept is necessary in almost all cases, since migrating components are normally at very low concentrations in any food and direct chemical / physical analysis almost impossible.

Dr. K. Figge, who has been one of the principal leaders in promoting and conducting migration studies (at Unilever), stated the problem of food simulant selection in its essence in a paper presented at the PIRA Seminar S13 in November 1978:

Natural migration must be simulated in model tests to

> determine the migrated or extracted additives and monomers in food simulants, which can more easily be analysed. However, the results of such migration or extraction studies are only then suitable for the assessment of the health-safety of plastics packagings if the conditions under which plastics packagings are in contact with the food in practice are simulated in the model tests sufficiently exactly. It is therefore necessary to fix test temperatures and times that are closely related to those of the practice. Moreover, contact media—so-called test foodstuffs—must be used which are comparable with the different foodstuffs regarding their behaviour towards plastics.

De Wilde (1967) in his review expresses similar sentiments.

Water, 3% acetic acid, and 10% aqueous ethanol were proposed as simulants for nonfatty foods by the FDA in 1955 and by the British Plastic Federation in 1962. As Haesen and Schwarze (1979) point out in their review, these solvents were readily available in pure form, and they could be evaporated to dryness to measure residues. In other early work, 0.1% NaCl, black tea, and even milk were used as aqueous food simulants.

Aqueous ethanol has always been selected to mimic alcoholic beverages—but this may not be suitable in some instances if the flavoring constituents of wines and other liquors affect migration rates.

Suitable simulants for fatty foods (or fat-releasing foods) still remains a major problem. *n*-Heptane, diethyl ether, ethanol, or paraffin oil have been widely used, but in many studies they have been shown to be unsuitable (Figge et al. 1968; Figge 1972). The studies at Unilever led to the development of a synthetic triglyceride (HB-307) based upon coconut oil, but with saturated fatty acids, which appears to simulate well natural oils and fatty foods. There still are difficulties, however, in analyzing small migrant concentrations in HB-307 unless radio-labeled tracers are employed. In other studies (Adcock 1980; Adcock et al. 1980), the approach to developing a fat simulant has followed a different course and solvent mixtures are proposed. (See section III.) At present the FDA still employs *n*-heptane, but allows the migration values to be divided by 5 (see section II) except in certain special situations.

Thus there is significant current activity in developing better food (particularly fat) simulants.

As developed in a later section, there are other areas of migration which present problems and are (or should be) under active investigation. Some of these include

(*a*) the appropriate design of accelerated migration tests;
(*b*) an agreement in the design and operation of extraction cells to allow interlaboratory comparisons;
(*c*) studies of migration into *real* foods (solid and semi-solid) to define better the mechanism of transfer and the possibility of partitioning;
(*d*) studies of migration rates to dry foods.

The current position is one of transit. Early studies (even in the 1970s) very often produced migration data of doubtful value (or of very limited use since test conditions were not well defined; see the critiques by Katan 1979, 1980). Until very recently, analytical modelling was rarely introduced. For example, even though migration has long been recognized as a "diffusion" phenomenon, in almost no case were the migration results correlated as a function of the square root of time! Analytical chemistry has made and is making massive strides so that concentrations in the ppb range are routinely measured. These advancements have sometimes led to stricter regulations in terms of allowable migrant concentration levels in food. Such changes, argues Shaw (1977), are not always appropriate, since "natural" food itself often contains a ppb level of undesirables.

In this report an attempt has been made to present a brief, overall assessment of the field of migration of chemicals from plastics to foods. The current FDA procedures and problems are summarized in section II, while the currently available analytical models are described and some experimental results given in sections III and IV. A summary with recommendations forms section V.

Thus the *problem* is to understand the migration of polymer oligomers and additives to foods. The *problems* relate to methods to achieve this goal by selection of appropriate experimental techniques with suitable food-simulating solvents. We must also extend our ability to model analytically the migration process so that realistic acceleration tests may be developed and experimental data scaled to allow for variations in use conditions with a minimum of additional experimentation.

II. The FDA: Requirements and Concerns

We are interested primarily in the procedures followed by the FDA in actions involving petitions for *indirect food additives*. These are defined as "substances which unintentionally become components of food from contact with food packaging materials or processing equipment." We shall also limit our discussion to situations wherein there is a new (i.e., not currently regulated) food additive. (For regulated additives, there are generally definite end-tests required to determine if a specific lot complies with the regulation for that additive.)

Petitions submitted to the FDA contain information divided in several definite areas:

1. Identity. In this section, the chemical identity of the materials involved are delineated, including C.A. registry numbers, trade names, formulas, and molecular weights (or distributions, if a polymer). A complete description of all potential food additives is required.* These may arise from unreacted raw materials, side reaction products, raw material impurities, catalysts, added adjuvants, low-molecular-weight oligomers, and so on. Both a listing and an estimate of the concentration in the final product is needed. Particular care is paid to substances known to be toxic or carcinogenic.

2. Usage. Documentation is necessary to indicate the usage of the product, i.e., the types of foods (see later discussion for listing), the use temperature (maximum), the weight of polymer (and thickness) to be used, and the weight of food / area of polymer.

3. Effect. Basically there is a requirement to show why the concentrations of any potential food additive cannot be reduced to even smaller values. A lower limit might be necessary, for example, with an antioxidant to accomplish its intended effect.

4. Methods of analysis. All methods of analysis used in any testing method must be described and the reliability stated.

5. Safety, toxicity, and environmental impact analyses. A discussion of these important issues is required based on the experimental migration test results and proposed end use. In some cases feeding studies are required.

A key part of the FDA petition is the experimental

*To be certain of potential food additives often requires very sophisticated methods of analysis. For example, Berg (1980) reported that some polyethylenes may contain traces of aromatic hydrocarbons with unsaturated side chains. The threshold values for an effect on product quality may be as low as 1 ppb in the polymer.

component to determine the expected migration of the food additive(s). Quoting directly from 1976 FDA Indirect Additive Guidelines:

> In general, practicable methods for the determination of indirect additives in raw, processed, and/or finished food are not available. Alternatively, petitioners may substitute data showing the *maximum* level of the indirect additive that could become a component of food from contact with containers and equipment by providing comprehensive extraction data with *food-simulating solvents*, which are assumed to reproduce the nature and amount of extraction of the indirect additive by the food.
>
> These maximum extraction data should be used to estimate the maximum as well as the average quantity of the petitioned food additive to be expected in individual foods or types of foods and also in the total daily diet of the consumer. These estimates should be based on the following:
>
> 1. The maximum (equilibrium) extraction levels of the additive as determined in the various simulating solvents.
> 2. Daily diet composition of aqueous, fatty, acidic and alcoholic foods.
> 3. Estimated maximum percentage of the daily diet packaged in paper, plastics, coating, etc. containing the petitioned additive. Examples of the calculations as well as the basis for packaging estimates should be provided.
>
> Such migration data enable FDA toxicologists to decide whether or not animal feeding studies will be required to establish the safety of the additive.

Thus the FDA recognizes the necessity of using food-simulating solvents, since analyses of small migrant concentrations in real foods is very difficult. It becomes imperative, therefore, to be able to select appropriate solvents and test conditions. Note also that "equilibrium" extraction is required. This may not be possible in some cases, a difficulty that is recognized by the FDA, as noted later.

The regulations also specify that in any extraction tests, one should use the *highest* expected additive concentration with a polymer of the *lowest* expected molecular weight range. The thickest expected polymer film (or coating) should also be used.

Regarding the test method, I again quote from the FDA guidelines: "Perform extractions on test specimens (e.g., films, bottles, panels, cans, etc.) according to the AOAC method,* or under immersion conditions or under other suitable testing conditions as dictated by the particular materials under study. In all cases, the extraction conditions must reflect the intended conditions of use."

In many instances, the test procedure involves preparing a stack of film specimens separated by screening and immersing this stack in the appropriate solvent for a given amount of time at the requisite test temperature. While in some cases reliable migration data are obtained, in other instances, the resulting value may be significantly lower than would have been obtained if the specimens were exposed to an agitated solvent. For cases in which the migrant is only slightly soluble in the solvent, partitioning or mass transfer effects may become important in the quiescent region between screens. In section III, I present data to buttress this assertion.

Temperatures used in the extraction tests are specified to be those "under the most severe conditions of temperature to which the additive is expected to be subjected. At a minimum, use 120° F (49° C)." In some instances,

***Official Methods of Analysis of the Association of Official Analytical Chemists*, 12th ed., 1975 (AOAC, Box 540, Benjamin Franklin Station, Washington, D.C. 20044), secs. 21.010–21.015.

lower-temperature testing is permitted if the food is cold-filled and refrigerated storage is required.

The normal FDA food-simulating solvents are shown below with the general class of foods which they are presumed to simulate:

Distilled water	Nonacid foods (pH above 5.0)
3% Acetic acid	Foods with pH 5.0 or below
8 or 50% Ethanol	Foods containing alcohol (actual alcohol concentration may be substituted)
n-Heptane	Fatty foods

When *n*-heptane is employed, the extraction results are to be divided by 5—presumably in acknowledgment of the fact that this hydrocarbon is a more efficacious solvent than fatty foods. A more detailed delineation of food types and specified extractants are shown in Tables 2.1 and 2.2.

Until recently, the test time was based on an equilibrium concept. One had to show that in three successive samples there had been no change in concentration of the additive. Samples of aqueous solvents were to be spaced by at least 24 hours, whereas for *n*-heptane, the intervals had to be at least 4 hours apart. If one wished to simulate a presterilization, then there was an initial extraction period followed by the "equilibrium extractions."

The total extractant is normally measured by evaporating the solvent to dryness and weighing the residue. Specific chemical analyses may then be carried out by suitable tests depending upon the additive.

Results are reported as mg extracted (at equilibrium) per square inch of surface. Generally one assumes there are 10 g food per square inch of contact surface to arrive at ppm in the food.

As a final note on the FDA guidelines, there is the following statement: "Generally, packaging of dry foods

Table 2.1. Types of Raw and Processed Foods

I. Nonacid, aqueous products; may contain salt or sugar or both (pH above 5.0).
II. Acid, aqueous products; may contain salt or sugar or both; includes oil-in-water emulsions of low- or high-fat content.
III. Aqueous, acid or nonacid products containing free oil or fat; may contain salt; includes water-in-oil emulsions of low- or high-fat content.
IV. Dairy products and modification:
  A. Water-in-oil emulsions, high- or low-fat.
  B. Oil-in-water emulsions, high- or low-fat.
V. Low-moisture fats and oils.
VI. Beverages:
  A. Containing up to 8 percent of alcohol.
  B. Nonalcoholic.
  C. Containing more than 8 percent of alcohol.
VII. Bakery products other than those included under types VIII or IX of this table:
  A. Moist bakery products with surface containing free fat or oil.
  B. Moist bakery products with surface containing no free fat or oil.
VIII. Dry solids with the surface containing no free fat or oil
IX. Dry solids with the surface containing free fat or oil.

Table 2.2. Extractants for Various Food Classes

	Water	3% acetic acid	Ethanol 8%	Ethanol 50%	*n*-heptane
I	X				
II		X			
III	X				X
IVA	X				X
IVB	X				
V					X
VIA			X		
VIB	X				
VIC				X	
VIIA					X
VIIB	X				
VIII			none		
IX					X

whose surface contains no free fat or oil results in very little migration, except where the abrasive nature of the food may result in some contamination. Extractions are not ordinarily required for additives to materials which contact only dry food." As we shall see in sections III and IV, recent test results suggest this issue be reconsidered.

The FDA has developed a workable process to screen new indirect food additives that is generally quite satisfactory in protecting the public without being overly restrictive. Many of the rules noted above, however, do not recognize the significant developments, both in theoretical modelling and in new experimental facts, that have occurred in the 1970s. It is to the credit of the FDA that the agency recognizes these shortcomings and has embarked on two major research studies with Arthur D. Little, Inc. of Cambridge, Massachusetts, and with the U.S. National Bureau of Standards to study both the fundamental mechanism of migration and to improve the correlation between extractions into food-simulating solvents and foods.

As an early result of these studies, current petitions must supply migration-time data. For example, for use conditions involving room-temperature fill and storage, the data should cover at least ten days at 120° F (49° C). Appropriate extrapolations are then carried out when necessary. It might be noted that these extraction conditions are more conservative than those in Europe under comparable use conditions, i.e., ten days at 40° C.

As the experimental data base and analytical capabilities increase, one might expect to see significant changes in future FDA regulations dealing with indirect food additives. As will be developed later in sections III, IV, and V, there are several areas of weakness that should receive some priority:

1. Test procedures should be modified to remove the

possibility of local partitioning or mass transfer resistance; migration results should be required to scale with area.

2. There may be no necessity of including in the food-simulating solvents 3% acetic acid in addition to water. All the data published to date show little difference between these two solvents.
3. A more appropriate fat solvent is needed. HB-307 as developed at Unilever clearly well simulates many vegetable oils, but there are still analytical problems in measuring dilute migrant concentrations in this material. The dual solvent mixture concept of Adcock (with, for example, THF and methanol) provides an attractive range of simulations, depending upon the THF concentration. A similar approach at the National Bureau of Standards with ethanol-water mixtures has produced encouraging preliminary results. Corn oil is not a satisfactory fat simulant because of the variation in composition and the difficulties in analysis.
4. More work needs to be done on clarifying the behavior of solid and semisolid foods. Migration data to these foods are few, and too often, there are concerns about the accuracy of the results. A better definition of diffusion and partition coefficient magnitudes is needed. The problem of migration to dry foods needs especial attention.
5. Awareness of migration oddities may lead to special test requirements. For example, as hypothesized later, migration may be significantly hindered in high sucrose foods. The role of small concentrations of essential oils in affecting migration needs attention. An explanation of migration in emulsions would be very desirable.

III. Analytical Modelling of the Migration Process

A. INTRODUCTION

Before mathematical models can be developed, a physical picture of the migration process must be developed and the relevant "forces" and "resistances" stipulated. The initial and boundary conditions applicable to the problem of interest must also be determined. In almost all cases, simplifications are introduced at the outset to make the problem tractable, and it is to be hoped that such assertions do not affect the results in a significant way. Thus, each individual problem is treated separately—although there is a very definite theme of continuity in all models. No general model yet exists which is universally applicable.

In this section I treat a number of possible cases to illustrate many of the key concepts. In section IV I illustrate the use of some of the model results to correlate experimental migration data for selected systems. In some portions I have used the approach of Reid et al. (1980).

I have divided the cases to be studied into three principal categories, depending upon the properties of the extractant phase:

1. *Well-mixed.* In this case there is no resistance to migrant transfer in the extractant. The concentration of migrant in the extractant is independent of position although it may be time-dependent.
2. *Diffusive.* In this case, the extractant phase has no convective motion. Migrant movement in this phase occurs only by diffusive processes.
3. *Convective boundary case.* At the interface between the extractant and the polymer, I hypothesize a finite resistance to mass transfer in a thin fluid

layer. The migrant concentration in the bulk extractant is, however, independent of position.

As subcases of these three principal divisions, I treat the polymer film to be either finite or infinite in thickness; similarly, the extractant phase can be assumed to be finite or infinite in extent.

The initial treatment neglects any *penetration* of the polymer by the extractant. This important effect is considered in some detail in section III.C. Thus, in section III.B, I have assumed an ideal polymer film that is flat and of such extent that edge effects are not important. There is only a single migrant present, and initially, it is homogeneously distributed. The diffusion coefficient of the migrant in the polymer is a function only of temperature and not of position or time. Fick's laws of diffusion are assumed applicable.

B. MATHEMATICAL MODELS FOR THE IDEAL POLYMER CASE

Since Fick's laws apply, then for all cases, *within the polymer*:

$$\frac{\partial C_p}{\partial t} = D_p \frac{\partial^2 C_p}{\partial x^2} \tag{2.1}$$

where C_p is the migrant concentration in the polymer, t is the time, D_p is the constant diffusion coefficient of the migrant within the polymer. x is the length variable and is positive as measured from the extractant-polymer interface into the polymer. The initial conditions are

$$C_p = C_{p_o} \qquad t = 0, x \geq 0 \tag{2.2a}$$

Also, at t=0, the concentration of the migrant in the extractant phase, C_s, is assumed to be zero, i.e.,

$$C_s = 0 \qquad t = 0, x < 0 \tag{2.2b}$$

Equation (2.1) is solved to express C_p as a function of x and t, and then eq. (2.3) is used to determine the flux of migrant, $\dot{M}_t$, from the polymer.

$$\dot{M}_t = D_p(\partial C_p/\partial x)_{x=0} \tag{2.3}$$

Also, at the extractant-polymer boundary, local equilibrium partitioning is assumed to occur so that

$$K = (C_s/C_p)_{x=0} \tag{2.4}$$

The partition coefficient K is taken to be invariant with concentration.

The total quantity of migrant lost from the polymer is then found by integrating $\dot{M}_t$ over the time period when extraction occurs.

$$M_t = \int_0^t \dot{M}_t \, dt \tag{2.5}$$

Eqs. (2.1) through (2.5) are used in all cases.

1. Extractant Well-Mixed

(a) Polymer Film of Infinite Thickness. For thick polymer films, there are two subcases, depending on whether the extractant phase is chosen as infinite in extent or finite. For the former the boundary condition

$$C_s = 0, \quad \text{any } t, \quad x < 0 \tag{2.6a}$$

is used with eqs. (2.1) through (2.5) to yield

$$M_t = 2C_{p_o}(D_p t/\pi)^{1/2} \tag{2.7}$$

M_t is the *total* quantity of migrant lost from the polymer per unit area of surface at time t (Crank 1975, p. 32).

Eqs. (2.5) and (2.6a) can be interpreted in a physical sense as stating that the concentration of migrant in the polymer is forced to attain a zero value at the polymer-extractant interface at all times after migration begins. Diffusive processes within the polymer then determine the rate of migration, and the properties of the extractant play no role. The migration is proportional to the square root of time and depends linearly on the initial concentration of migrant in the polymer.

If there is a limited quantity of extractant, measured by the term a, the extractant volume to transfer area ratio, then eq. (2.6a) is replaced by

$$a \frac{dC_s}{dt} = D_p \frac{\partial C_p}{\partial x}\bigg|_{x=0} \tag{2.6b}$$

which states that the flux of migrant from the polymer increases the migrant concentration in the extractant, but with no concentration gradients in the extractant. With eqs. (2.1) through (2.5) and (2.6b) (Carslaw and Jaeger 1959, p. 306),

$$M_t = aKC_{p_o}(1 - e^{z^2} \operatorname{erfc} z) \tag{2.8}$$

where

$$z = (D_p t)^{1/2}/aK \tag{2.9}$$

In dimensionless form eq. (2.8) becomes

$$M_t^* = M_t/aKC_{p_o} = 1 - e^{z^2} \operatorname{erfc} z \tag{2.10}$$

M_t^* represents the ratio of the migrant concentration in the extractant, compared to the maximum attainable concentration when the migrant has attained a partition equilibrium with the polymer *at the original migrant concentration in the polymer*, C_{p_o}. M_t^* cannot exceed unity. M_t^* is plotted as a function of z in Figure 2.1. For values of z less than about 0.05, eq. (2.10) can be simplified to

$$M_t^* \sim 2z/\sqrt{\pi}, \qquad z < 0.05 \tag{2.11}$$

or

$$M_t \sim 2C_{p_o}(D_p t/\pi)^{1/2} \tag{2.12}$$

Eq. (2.12) is identical to eq. (2.7) and reflects the fact that at low values of z, partitioning effects are negligible and the rate of migration is determined solely by the diffusional processes in the polymer.

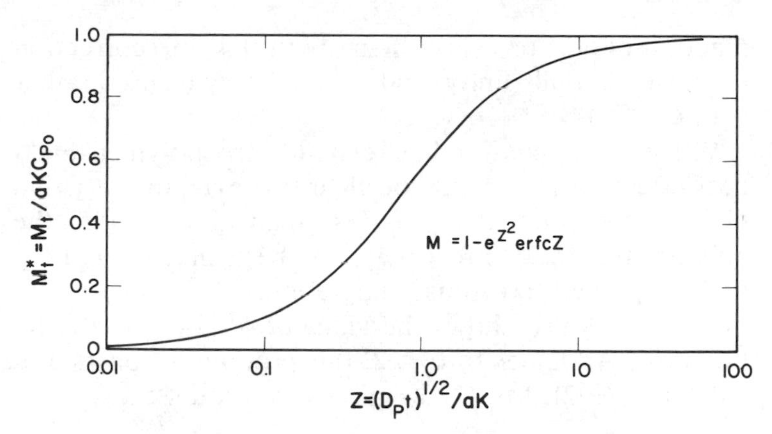

Figure 2.1—Migration for a well-mixed, finite-volume extractant.

(b) Polymer Film of Finite Thickness. If the film is contacted by extractant on both sides (the usual situation in migration testing), we define the film half-thickness as L and impose the condition:

$$D_p(\partial C_p/\partial x)_{z=L} = 0 \qquad (2.13)$$

(If only one-sided extraction is carried out, then L becomes the thickness of the film.)

For this finite polymer film contacting an *infinite quantity of extractant*, eqs. (2.1) through (2.5) are used with eqs. (2.6a) and (2.13) to yield (Carslaw and Jaeger 1959, p. 128):

$$M_t = 2C_{p_o}(D_p t/\pi)\, F(\psi) \qquad (2.14)$$

where

$$F(\psi) = (\pi/4\psi)^{1/2}\,[1 - 2\sum_{n=1}^{\infty} (e^{-q_n^2\psi})\,/q_n^2] \qquad (2.15)$$

$$\psi = D_p t/L^2 \qquad (2.16)$$

$$q_n = (2n-1)\pi/2 \qquad (2.17)$$

If eq. (2.14) is compared to eq. (2.7), it will be obvious that the term $F(\psi)$ corrects the correlation for finite polymer thicknesses. On Figure 2.2, $F(\psi)$ is plotted as a function of ψ. For ψ less than about 0.4, the correction term is essentially unity, and eq. (2.7) may be used rather than eq. (2.14).

While the discussion has related to the polymer thickness effect on ψ, it should be clear that even for very thin films, if the product $D_p t$ is less than about $0.4L^2$, the polymer thickness effect may also be neglected and eq. (2.7) employed to estimate migration.

Figure 2.2 also shows the value of $\psi^{1/2} F(\psi)$ as a function of ψ. At values of $\psi < 2$, this product is constant at 0.886 ($=\sqrt{\pi}/2$). Eq. (2.14) may be rewritten as

$$M_t = (2/\sqrt{\pi}) C_{p_o} L \, [\psi^{1/2} F(\psi)] \tag{2.18}$$

Thus, for $\psi > 2$, $M_t \sim C_{p_o} L$, i.e., the quantity of migrant lost is equal to that originally in the polymer. No further migration is then possible.

The conclusions to be drawn from the finite polymer–infinite extractant case is that for values of $\psi <$

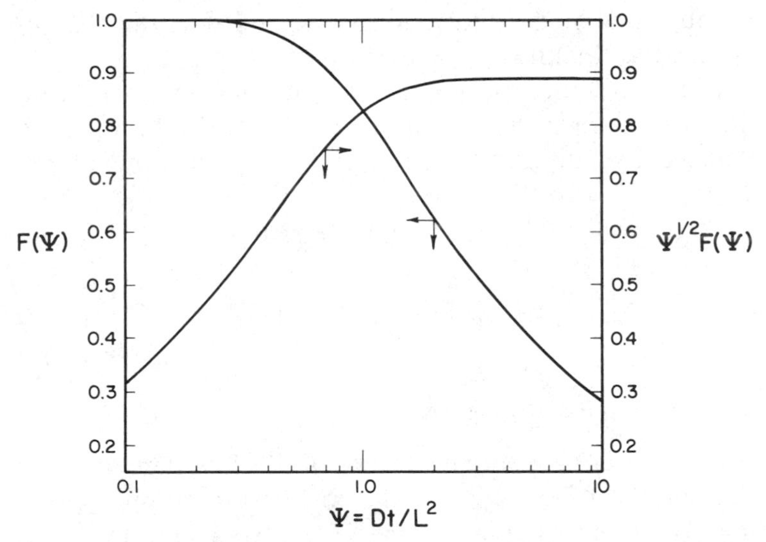

Figure 2.2—Effect of polymer thickness for infinite extractant case.

0.4, the model reverts to the infinite polymer–infinite extractant case, while for $\psi > 2$, complete extraction has occurred.

When *both* the polymer and extractant are finite (Carslaw and Jaeger 1959, p. 128):

$$M_t = C_{p_o} L \left[\frac{\alpha}{1+\alpha} - 2 \sum_{n=1}^{\infty} \frac{\exp(-p_n^2 \psi)}{(p_n{}^2 + \frac{1}{\alpha} + \frac{1}{\alpha^2}} \right] \qquad (2.19)$$

ψ is defined in eq. (2.16) and p_n is given by the roots of the equation

$$\tan p_n = \alpha p_n \qquad (2.20)$$

with

$$\alpha = aK/L \qquad (2.21)$$

The finiteness of the extractant is introduced through the term a (the volume of extractant per unit area of transfer), while the capacity of the extractant for the migrant enters through the partition coefficient K [see eq. (2.4)].

Migration values calculated from eq. (2.19) are shown in Figure 2.3. The ordinate is the fraction of migrant transferred to the extractant. The abscissa, ψ, is the same parameter used in Figure 2.2, and the various curves reflect differing values of α. Consider first the upper curve for $\alpha > 100$. This would normally represent the case where either the extractant was a good solvent for the migrant or there was a large quantity of extractant (large a). In this situation, the *infinite* extractant case would be applicable. But, from Figure 2.2 it has already been shown that if $\psi < 0.4$, eq. (2.7) could be used. In fact, writing eq. (2.7) in terms of the variables used in Figure 2.3,

$$M_t / C_{p_o} L = (2/\sqrt{\pi})^{1/2} \qquad (2.22)$$

so that for $\psi < 0.4$, the upper curve has a slope of 0.5. One concludes that for $\alpha > 10$ and $\psi < 0.4$, eq. (2.7) may be used rather than eq. (2.19).

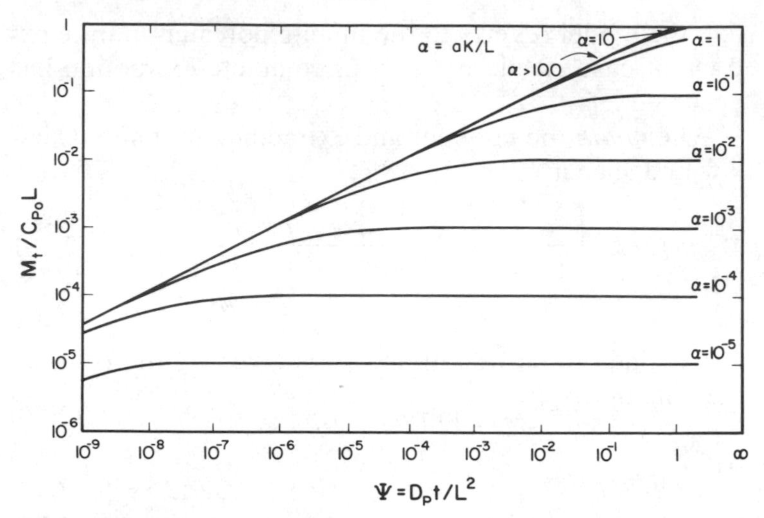

Figure 2.3—Migrant transfer for a well-mixed extractant, finite extractant–finite polymer case.

Next, for lower values of α, one notes (in Figure 2.3) that the fraction migrated asymptotes at a value close to α. This, of course, represents a partitioning. For small α (where little migrant is lost), such a partitioning indicates that

$$M_t/C_{p_o}L \cong \alpha = aK/L$$

or

$$M_t = aKC_{p_o} \tag{2.23}$$

For larger values of α, the asymptote is not exactly equal to α, since partitioning occurs with a value of $C_p(x=0) < C_{p_o}$.

Figure 2.3 allows a rapid scan of the migration region of interest depending upon values of D_p, K, *a*, L, and t. The entire region of interest in Figure 2.2 ($0.4 < \psi < 2$) is compressed to a very small domain in Figure 2.3. One concludes that only rarely is it necessary to employ the complex relation, eq. (2.19).

2. Immobile Extractant Phase

When there is no mixing or stirring of the extractant phase (or it may be a solid), all migrant transfer into this phase from the polymer must occur by diffusive processes. Eqs. (2.1) through (2.5) still apply, but instead of eqs. (2.6a) or (2.6b), we have

$$\frac{\partial C_s}{\partial t} = D_s \frac{\partial^2 C_s}{\partial x^2} \tag{2.24}$$

and

$$D_p \frac{\partial C_p}{\partial x} = D_s \frac{\partial C_s}{\partial x}, \quad x = 0 \tag{2.25}$$

where D_s is the diffusion coefficient of the migrant in the extractant. It is assumed to be a function of temperature only. There are again two subcases of interest, i.e., when the extractant phase is finite in extent and when it is infinite. In both, we assume the polymer is of infinite thickness.

(a) Extractant Phase of Infinite Extent. When the ratio of extractant volume to transfer area, a, is very large, the necessary boundary condition, in addition to eq. (2.3), is

$$C_s = 0, \quad \text{any } t, \quad x \to -\infty \tag{2.26}$$

In this case (Crank 1975, p. 39),

$$M_t = \frac{2C_{p_o}\beta}{(1 + \beta)} (D_p t/\pi)^{1/2} \tag{2.27}$$

where

$$\beta = K(D_s/D_p)^{1/2} \tag{2.28}$$

Consider the case of $\beta >> 1$, which might result from a very small migrant diffusion coefficient in the polymer, a large diffusion coefficient in the solvent, or from large values of the partition coefficient, i.e., when migrants are quite soluble in the extractant phase. In this case $\beta/$

$(1+\beta) \rightarrow 1$ and eq. (2.27) simplifies to eq. (2.7). For such situations, migration is controlled by diffusive processes in the polymer, and the specific properties of the solvent play no role.

The opposite case of small β is also of interest. In such a situation, K is normally a very small number, i.e., the migrant is very slightly soluble in the extractant. Then, $\beta/(1+\beta) \rightarrow \beta$ and eq. (2.27) becomes:

$$M_t = 2C_{p_o}K(D_s t/\pi)^{1/2} \tag{2.29}$$

Here, no properties of the polymer appear, and the migration depends entirely upon diffusive processes within the extractant phase. The term $(C_{p_o}K)$ represents the interfacial concentration of migrant *on the extractant* side and is a constant in this limiting case.

(b) Extractant Phase of Limited Extent. When there is a limited amount of extractant, eqs. (2.1) through (2.5), with (2.24) and (2.25), still apply, but eq. (2.26) is replaced by

$$D_s \frac{\partial C_s}{\partial x} = 0, \quad x = a \tag{2.30}$$

where a is the thickness of the immobile extractant phase measured from the polymer-extractant boundary. In a flat-sheet situation, a is again the volume of extractant per unit area of transfer surface. By modifying the heat transfer results of Ehrenburg (1932) and Lovering (1936),

$$M_t = \frac{2C_{p_o}\beta}{1+\beta}(D_p t/\pi)^{1/2} \times \left\{1 - \frac{2}{1+\beta}\sum_{n=1}^{\infty} \left[-\frac{(1-\beta)}{(1+\beta)}\right]^{n-1} e^{-n^2W^2}[1 - E(nW)]\right\} \tag{2.31}$$

where β was defined earlier by eq. (2.28) and

$$W = aK/\beta(D_p t)^{1/2} = a/(D_s t)^{1/2} = (z\beta)^{-1} \tag{2.32}$$

$$E(W) = (\pi)^{1/2} W e^{W^2} \operatorname{erfc} W \tag{2.33}$$

The leading term of eq. (2.31) is identical to that found for the infinite extractant case, eq. (2.27), and the term in braces represents the effect of partitioning on the migration. At short times (or for large values of W) the term in braces is essentially unity, and the migration can be simulated as from an infinitely thick immobile extractant phase. At very long times (or for small values of W), the term in braces reduces to $(1+\beta)W(\pi)^{1/2}/2$, so that

$$M_t = aKC_{p_o}, \quad t \rightarrow \infty \text{ (or } W \rightarrow 0) \qquad (2.34)$$

In this limit, the immobile extractant phase has no migrant concentration gradient and is partitioned with the polymer at the initial migrant concentration in the polymer, C_{p_o}.

A convenient way to visualize the predictions of eq. (2.31) is to compare M_t both to the infinite immobile extractant case and to the well-mixed finite extractant case, eq. (2.8) or eq. (2.10). We rearrange to introduce the variables M_t^* and z. As defined by eq. (2.10), M_t^* is a dimensionless parameter which yields the fraction of migrant lost compared to the value when equilibrium partitioning has occurred. z is a dimensionless time given by eq. (2.9). Then, eq. (2.31) becomes:

$$M_t^* = \frac{2}{\sqrt{\pi}(1+\beta)} \beta z \left\{ 1 - \frac{2}{1+\beta} \sum_{n=1}^{\infty} \left[-\frac{(1-\beta)}{(1+\beta)} \right]^{n-1} e^{-n^2/\beta^2 z^2} \left[1 - E\left(\frac{n}{\beta z} \right) \right] \right\} \qquad (2.35)$$

In this form, M_t^* is a function only of β and z. Solutions to this equation for M_t^* are shown in Figure 2.4.

For large values of β, the $M_t^* - z$ relation is given by the curve marked $\beta = \infty$. This is the same curve shown in Figure 2.1 for M_t^* vs. z for a *well-mixed* solvent. Clearly, this should be the case, since large values of β infer that the migrant diffusion is rapid in the extractant relative to

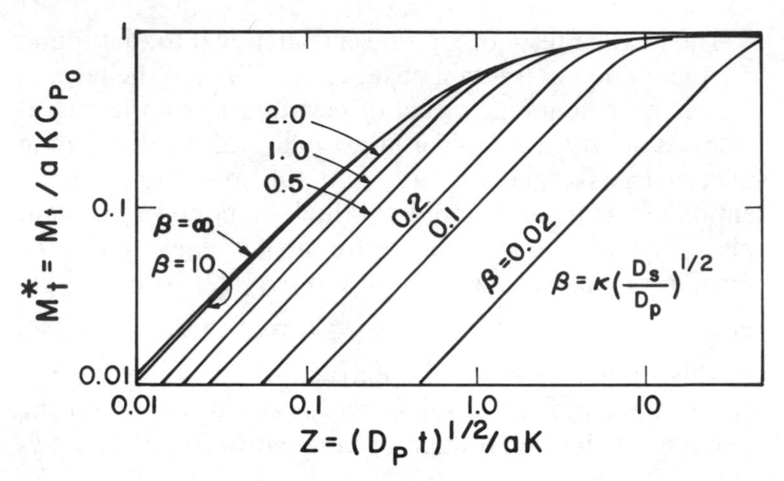

Figure 2.4—Migration for an immobile, finite-volume extractant.

the polymer, and in the limiting case, the extractant would appear "well mixed" even though only diffusive processes were active. Even with β values of 5 or more, there is little difference between well-mixed and diffusive cases—at least over the range of z shown.

For all values of β, there is a linear $M_t^* - z$ correlation in the lower z range, and significant curvature is not exhibited until z becomes sufficiently large that partitioning becomes important; then, each β line curves and approaches the β=∞ (or well-mixed) curve in an asymptotic fashion. The slope of the β lines in the linear region is unity, and the thickness or extent of the extractant phase is not relevant.

In summary, when considering immobile extractants, if $\beta > 2$, the extractant may be considered well mixed and the models developed in III.B.1 may be employed. Even if $\beta < 2$, if $\beta z < \sim 0.6$, the extent of the extractant phase is unimportant, and eq. (2.27) may be used.

3. Convective Boundary Layer Present

To this point we have considered two limiting cases, a well-mixed extractant and an immobile extractant. A question often raised is, When is the extractant well-mixed and what intensity of agitation is required to attain this state? We treat this intermediate case in a somewhat simplified manner—which, however, illustrates the important concepts. That is, we assume the extractant phase is of infinite extent (to eliminate partitioning considerations) and model it as being completely well-mixed *except* for a boundary layer adjacent to the polymer. Mass transfer of migrant from the polymer then occurs by diffusion across the boundary layer into the bulk extractant (which, being infinite in extent, has a constant migrant concentration that can be assumed to be zero). The more vigorous the stirring in the extractant phase, the thinner the boundary layer thickness. When the thickness is chosen to be zero, we have the well-mixed case. The analytical model employs eqs. (2.1) through (2.5) with eq. (2.35)

$$D_p \frac{\partial C_p}{\partial x} = kKC_p \quad x = 0 \tag{2.35}$$

Eq. (2.35) states that the flux of migrant from the polymer is equal to the product of the mass transfer coefficient, k, and the driving force across the boundary layer. This driving force is the difference between the migrant concentration in the extractant at the polymer interface (KC_p) and in the bulk, assumed to be zero. The solution for this case is (Crank 1975, p. 36):

$$M_t = 2C_{p_o}(D_p t/\pi)^{1/2} \left\{1 - \frac{1}{2Y}\left[\sqrt{\pi} - \frac{E(Y)}{Y}\right]\right\} \tag{2.36}$$

where

$$Y = \beta^2 (D_p t)^{1/2}/K\delta \tag{2.37}$$

$$E(Y) = \sqrt{\pi}\, Y e^{Y^2} \operatorname{erfc} Y \tag{2.38}$$

and δ is the effective boundary layer thickness. δ is related to the mass transfer coefficient k by

$$k = D_s/\delta \tag{2.39}$$

with D_s the diffusion coefficient of the migrant in the extractant. β and K were defined earlier in eqs. (2.28) and (2.5) respectively.

As eq. (2.29) is arranged, we can see that the term in braces is the ratio of M_t to the value of M_t for a well-mixed case with an infinite quantity of extractant, eq. (2.7). We call this ratio M^+. In Figure 2.5, values of M^+ are shown as a function of the parameter Y. If Y is greater than about 5, the extractant phase can be considered as well-mixed and eq. (2.7) employed. Note that this state may be attained by very small values of the boundary layer thickness, δ, as well as for long times.

Next, consider the opposite case of low Y. As seen in Figure 2.5, for this range, M^+ varies linearly with Y. It can be shown, for low Y,

$$1 - \frac{1}{2Y}\left[\sqrt{\pi} - \frac{E(Y)}{Y}\right] \rightarrow \frac{\sqrt{\pi}}{2} Y, \quad \text{low } Y \tag{2.40}$$

Then

$$M_t \rightarrow C_{p_o} K (D_s/\delta) t = C_{p_o} K k t \tag{2.41}$$

The interesting result obtained is that the quantity of migrant lost is now proportional to time. Eq. (2.41) results from combining eqs. (2.4) and (2.35), and integrating assuming $C_p(x=0) \approx C_{p_o}$, an assertion which is quite reasonable at short times.

At small Y the assumption of a well-mixed system can be a very poor approximation.

In a practical vein, one might query when it is necessary to be concerned about a finite mass transfer resistance in an ''agitated'' solvent. To help answer this question, consider four typical extremes:

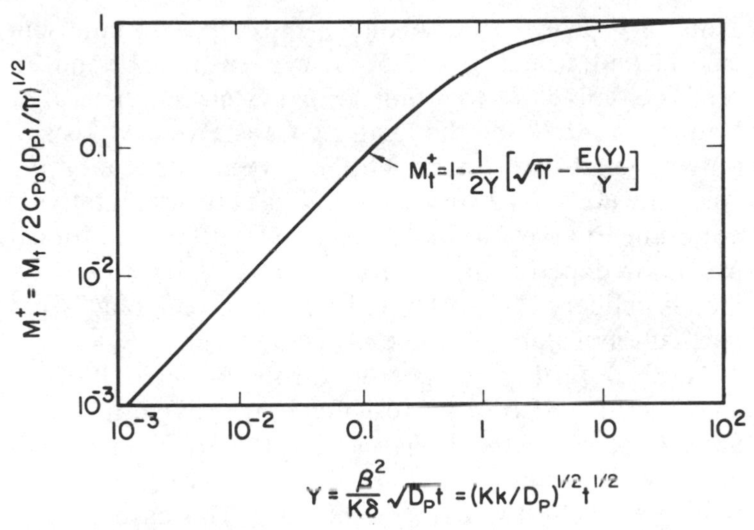

Figure 2.5—Migration for an extractant with a mass transfer resistance.

Case	D_p (cm²/s)	*K*
A	10^{-14}	10^{-2}
B	10^{-14}	10^{-4}
C	10^{-9}	10^{-2}
D	10^{-9}	10^{-4}

The lower of the values of the migrant diffusion coefficient in the polymer might correspond to cases with a glassy polymer, while the higher value would be more typical of a rubbery polymer. The larger of the two partition coefficients might apply to a migrant which was reasonably soluble in the extractant, and the lower, to a slightly soluble case. For all, we set the migrant diffusion coefficient in the extractant as $\approx 10^{-5}\text{cm}^2/\text{s}$ and as discussed later, we let $\delta \approx 10^{-2}$cm. Then

Case	$\beta = K(D_s/D_p)^{1/2}$	$Y/\sqrt{t}$
A	316	100
B	3.16	1
C	1.0	0.32
D	10^{-2}	3×10^{-3}

Thus, if $t=1$ hr=3,600 seconds, Y exceeds 10 in all but case D, and, from Figure 2.5, the systems may be considered well-mixed at this time. For system D, even after 10 days, $Y \approx 2.8$, and the quantity transferred, M_t, is still only about 70% of what might have been expected if the solvent were stirred very vigorously. Thus we tentatively conclude that reasonable agitation suffices for most migration experiments except for those where the polymer is rubbery (large D_p) and where the migrant is not particularly soluble in the extractant.

To place further perspective on the possible effect of an external mass transfer resistance, we have drawn Figure 2.6 for case D and have varied the effective boundary layer thickness from 0 to 10^{-1}cm for a polymer containing initially 100 ppm of migrant. The case of $\delta=0$ reduces to the well-mixed, infinite extractant case, eq. (2.7). As the effective boundary layer thickness is increased, the quantity of migrant lost decreases, and the difference is largest in the early time period. Thus, early time-migration data, for this case, would be very sensitive to the exact agitation conditions for the extractant and polymer system. There is also a lower limit for the migration, i.e., when the extractant is immobile and only diffusion occurs [eq. (2.27)]. It may be noted, in Figure 2.6, that the pure diffusion limit and the $\delta=10^{-1}$ cm curve would apparently cross at some time <1 hour. This is an artifact of the models, however, since, *at very short times* with large effective boundary layer thicknesses, the boundary conditions for the external mass-transfer case are invalid. Refer to eq. (2.35); this relation states that at time zero, there is instantaneously established a boundary layer (of thickness δ) across which diffusion of the migrant occurs. No allowance is made for the establishment of this boundary layer nor for the migrant within it. Thus, at very short times, the model is not valid. The pure diffusion model, on the other hand, does allow the development of a concentration profile of migrant within the (immobile) extractant phase.

In Figure 2.6, the time axis is extended only to about one day. This limit was selected as a practical one, since,

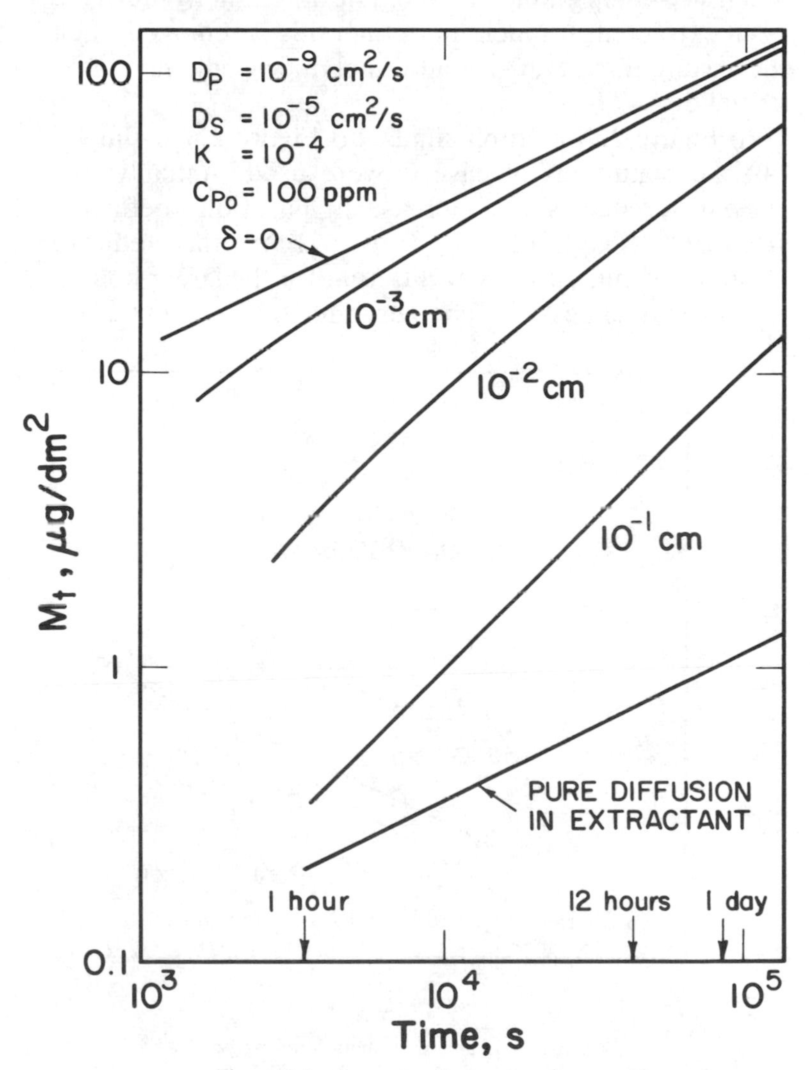

Figure 2.6—Example of migration for case D.

for the assumed properties of the extractant and polymer, diffusion is rapid. Only for thick, real polymer films would longer times be meaningful. In fact, if the polymer film were 1 mm thick and contacted only on one side, when $M_t = 100 \mu g/dm^2$, 10% of the migrant would have been extracted. If much more than this is removed, then the assumption of an "infinite" polymer would no longer be valid.

In Figure 2.7, a graph similar to Figure 2.6 is shown, but the conditions of case C were used. Actually, the only difference is the increase in partition coefficient from 10^{-4} (Fig. 2.6) to 10^{-2} (Fig. 2.7). Yet the predicted quantity of migrant is very different for the larger boundary layer thicknesses. (The curve for $\delta = 0$ is identical in

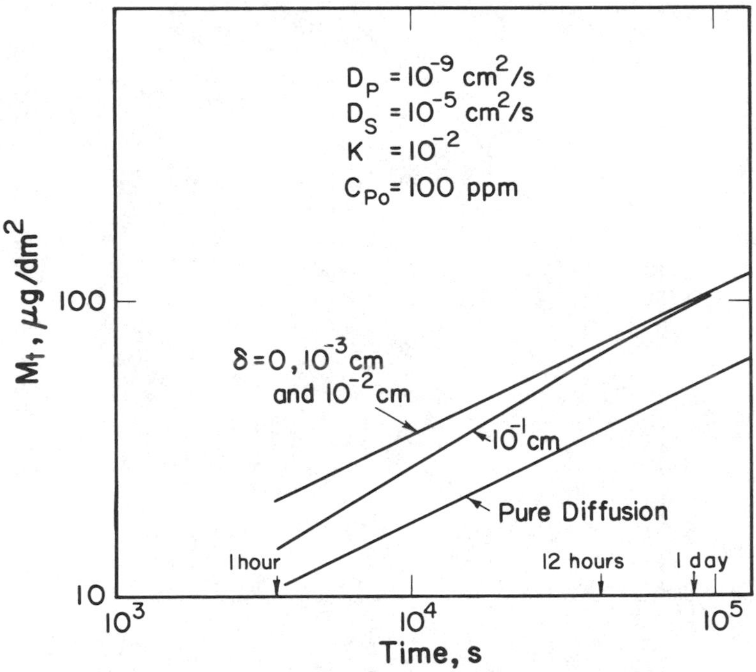

Figure 2.7—Example of migration for case C.

both figures.) For the conditions in Figure 2.7, external boundary layer resistances are significant only when they are reasonably large (circa 0.1 cm) and at short times. In this instance the well-mixed ($\delta=0$) and diffusion cases differ only by a factor of 2, since $\beta=1$ and $\beta/(1+\beta)=\frac{1}{2}$. As noted earlier, for case C, even slight stirring would allow one to assume the extractant was well-mixed.

Paul and McSpadden (1976) have employed eq. (2.36) to model drug release from a polymer matrix and tested the equation by diffusing Sudan III red dye from a vulcanized silicone rubber into agitated acetone with a magnetic stirrer. When M_t was plotted as a function of $t^{1/2}$, curves were obtained which were similar in shape to Figure 2.6—i.e., at short times, M_t was proportional to time. Their data were correlated with a mass transfer coefficient of about 3.4×10^{-4}cm/s. Using eq. (2.39) and an estimated diffusion coefficient of Sudan III dye in acetone to be $\sim10^{-6}$cm^2/s, an effective boundary layer thickness of $\sim3\times10^{-3}$cm is obtained.

Eisenberg and associates (1955) measured mass transfer coefficients for rotating cylinders and correlated their data with the peripheral velocity of the cylinder and a Reynolds number based on rotor diameter. Peripheral velocities varied from 6 to 300 cm/s and over this range, effective boundary layer thicknesses were about 2×10^{-2} to 3×10^{-3}cm. Later studies (Bennett and Lewis 1958; Holman and Ashar 1971; Smith and Colton 1972) present more complete theoretical results for well-defined geometries. Usually, however, for any specific migration test cell, dissolution or electrode-reaction experiments are necessary to provide a guide to the boundary layer thickness which would be applicable. Nevertheless, in most extraction cells, agitation is not particularly vigorous, and δ values in the range of 0.01 cm might be typical.

C. EFFECT OF EXTRACTION PENETRATION UPON MIGRATION

The analytical models developed in the previous section assumed no penetration of the polymer by the extractant—or, if any did occur, there was no appreciable swelling, and the migrant diffusion coefficient could still be assumed constant. In this section, I relax these constraints.

Initially I describe the results of two studies wherein analytical models are developed for the case of a migrant moving into the extractant phase while, at the same time, the extractant penetrates the polymer film. In both of these analyses, the polymer and extractant phases were taken to be infinite in extent.

Later, I will examine briefly the current literature dealing with general solvent penetration of polymers and point out some interesting results which suggest that modelling of penetrating extractants may be quite difficult.

1. Introduction

In crystalline polymers above their glass transition temperatures, the diffusion coefficient of most migrants is very low in comparison to the diffusion coefficients of the same material in aqueous or organic solvents. Ratios of the diffusion coefficients of 10^{-8} would not be uncommon. Thus, in a large fraction of relevant migration studies, one would hypothesize that control was completely in the polymer phase, and the external phase composition would be unimportant. Clearly, this is not the case. The primary reason why the external phase composition is important is that certain classes of extractants apparently can penetrate the polymer matrix and thereby modify drastically the local environment for migrant diffusion.

In the actual case, the process is (or can be) very complex. For foods in particular, only certain components enter the polymer—and this may result in a discontinuity in the penetrant composition at the interface and a composition gradient in both the polymer and food phase. Although pure extractants are not plagued by such problems, they may swell the polymer, and this occurs under kinetic restraints; i.e., the ingress of a component into a polymer may be governed by a combination of Fickian laws and chemical rate step(s).

In many published migration studies, these complicating problems are generally ignored. The penetrant is assumed to have some fixed, equilibrium value at the polymer film interface (presumably the equilibrium saturation value). It diffuses in the polymer following Fickian kinetics. The penetrant diffusion coefficient may or may not be a function of the penetrant concentration—but the diffusion coefficient of the migrant is normally assumed to depend upon the local concentration of the penetrant.

Practically speaking, the penetrant equilibrium concentration for cases of interest would be from about 10 to 40%. Values lower than 10% would approach the non-penetrating cases discussed in the previous section. Values much above 40% would probably not be encountered, since plastics exhibiting such levels of absorption would be modified so much as to be unsuitable as a packaging material.

In most published analyses, two regions of the polymer are delineated: the swollen region which contains penetrant and the unswollen region which does not. For simplicity in modelling, there is normally assumed to be a relatively sharp dividing plane between the two regions, and at this plane, the penetrant concentration drops essentially to zero and remains at this level at greater depths. The position of the swollen-unswollen plane varies with time.

The migrant has a diffusion coefficient in the unswollen region different from that in the swollen region. Often the former is assumed to be so small that it can be neglected; in the swollen zone, as noted earlier, the migrant diffusivity is normally chosen to be a function of the penetrant composition.

2. Knibbe Analysis

Knibbe (1971) analyzed the case where the diffusion coefficient of the migrant in the unswollen zone of the polymer was essentially zero while it was a *constant* value D_p^s in the swollen region. A well-stirred extractant case was chosen with the interfacial migrant concentration equal to zero. Knibbe states without proof that the swollen-unswollen plane penetrates into the polymer according to the relation

$$X = 2\eta_X\sqrt{t} \tag{2.42}$$

where η_X is a characteristic constant for the system and X is the depth of the plane. With eq. (2.42), one can employ Knibbe's calculated migrant concentration profile to determine the quantity of migrant lost per unit area at time t,

$$M_t = 2C_{p_o}\frac{(D_p t/\pi)^{1/2}}{W(\phi)} \tag{2.43}$$

where

$$\phi = \eta_X/\sqrt{D_p} \tag{2.44}$$

$$W(\phi) = 1 + \left[\frac{1}{E(\phi)} - 1\right] \text{erfc } \phi \tag{2.45}$$

$$E(\phi) = \pi\,\phi\,e^{\phi^2}\,\text{erfc } \phi \tag{2.46}$$

D_p is the (constant) diffusion coefficient of the migrant in the swollen region of the polymer. Note that if ϕ is large

($\eta_X > \sqrt{D_p}$), then $E(\phi) \approx 1$ so $W(\phi) \approx 1$ and eq. (2.43) reduces to the same equation that would have been obtained if penetration had been neglected. In this case, the migrant concentration at X is essentially C_{p_o}. ϕ values in excess of 3 or 4 are considered large.

For smaller values of ϕ, $W(\phi) < 1$, M_t increases; also, in such cases, the migrant concentration at X becomes less than C_{p_o} and the diffusive driving force in the swollen region decreases. In both cases, however, M_t is proportional to the square root of time.

Arguments will be presented below to relate η_X to the square root of the average penetrant diffusion coefficient in the polymer; thus, in some ways, the parameter $W(\phi)$ can be considered to depend on the ratio of diffusion coefficients of the penetrant and migrant in the swollen region of the polymer.

3. Rudolph Analysis

In a number of recent papers (Rudolph 1979; Rudolph 1980*a*, 1980*b*; vom Bruck et al. 1979; Figge and Rudolph 1979), Rudolph and his coworkers at Unilever have presented detailed models for the migrating process with a penetrating extractant. The Rudolph 1979 paper develops the basic equations, but swelling is not included; the extension to the swelling case was given in Rudolph 1980*a*.

Since a number of interesting results can be obtained from these papers, it is necessary to consider them in some detail. To minimize the complexity initially, let us take the simpler case where no swelling occurs and first develop expressions to describe the extractant penetration process. These may be compared later with the results of other investigators. After the extractant profiles are determined, we will examine the movement of migrant.

The physical model assumes an infinite quantity of well-mixed extractant (A) in contact with a polymer (B).* The extractant-polymer boundary is at x = 0 with positive x measured into the (infinitely thick) polymer. For the solvent penetration, it is assumed that the penetrant (extractant) diffusion coefficient D_A^B is constant.† The initial and boundary conditions are

$$c_A^B = 0 \qquad x \geq 0,\ t=0 \tag{2.47}$$

$$c_A^A = C_A^A \qquad x<0,\ \text{all } t \tag{2.48}$$

$$c_A^B(0,t) = KC_A^A = \text{constant} \tag{2.49}$$

$$c_A^B(X,t) = C_A^B = \text{constant} \tag{2.50}$$

Eq. (2.49) indicates that the penetrant concentration *in the polymer* at x=0 is a constant. The value would normally be found from the partition coefficient and C_A^A—or c_A^B (0) may be the saturation concentration of the extractant in the polymer. Finally, eq. (2.50) specifies that the swelling front is of "finite" thickness [X(t)], and at this position, the penetrant concentration is a constant (C_A^B). For x > X, C_A^B=0. Thus for 0<x<X(t),

$$\frac{\partial c_A}{\partial t}(x,t) = D_A^B \frac{\partial^2 c_A^B}{\partial x^2} \tag{2.51}$$

while at x=X, the flux of extractant (A) to this boundary equals the gain in A due to the movement of the boundary, i.e.,

$$D_A^B \left(\frac{\partial c_A^B}{\partial x} \right)_{t,\ x=X(t)} = -C_A^B \frac{dX(t)}{dt} \tag{2.52}$$

*Rudolph's analysis allowed for diffusive transfer in the extractant, but to illustrate the key points, I have chosen a well-mixed external phase.

†Subscripts represent components; superscripts show phases. Subscript *C*, introduced later, indicates the migrant. See Fig. 2.8 for a schematic showing concentrations in various regions.

To solve the diffusion equations, a transformation is made to Boltzmann's space with the variable η,

$$\eta = x/2\sqrt{t} \tag{2.53}$$

Then eq. (2.51) becomes

$$-2\eta \frac{dc_A^B}{d\eta} = D_A^B \frac{d^2 c_A^B}{d\eta^2} \quad 0<\eta<\eta_X \tag{2.54}$$

and the solution is

$$c_A^B(\eta) = \alpha \operatorname{erf}(\eta/\sqrt{D_A^B}) + \beta \tag{2.55}$$

but, from eq. (2.47), $\eta = 0$, $c_A^B = KC_A^A$, so

$$\beta = KC_A^A \tag{2.56}$$

At $\eta = \eta_X$, $c_A^B = C_A^B$, and

$$(C_A^B - KC_A^A)/\alpha = \operatorname{erf}(\eta_X/\sqrt{D_A^B}) \tag{2.57}$$

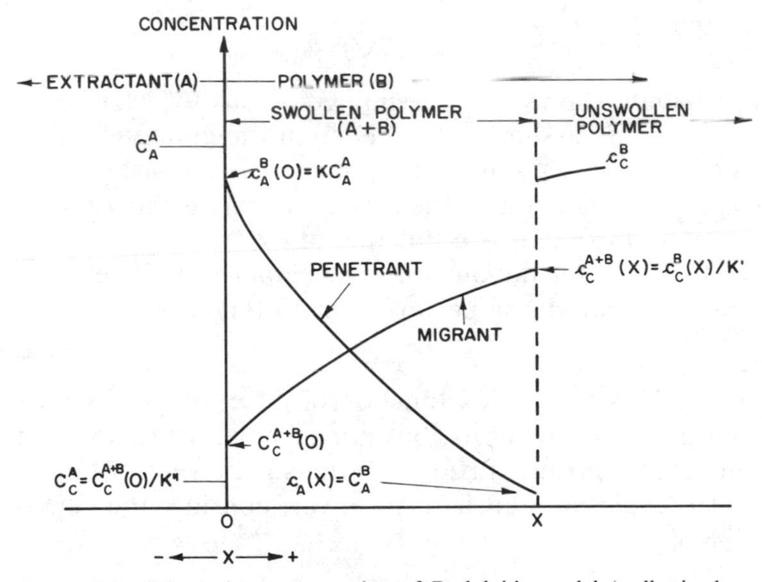

Figure 2.8—Schematic representation of Rudolph's model (well-mixed extractant, no-swelling case).

Since the left-hand side of eq. (2.57) is a constant, then

$$\eta_X = X/2\sqrt{t} = \text{constant} \qquad (2.58)$$

Therefore, the swelling front moves at a velocity proportional to $t^{-1/2}$ as postulated earlier by Knibbe. [See eq. (2.42).]

Also, by combining eqs. (2.55), (2.56), and (2.57), eliminating α and using eq. (2.52),

$$\sqrt{\pi}\, w\ e^{w^2} \operatorname{erf} w = y/(1-y) \qquad (2.59)$$

with

$$w = \eta_X/\sqrt{D_A^B} \qquad (2.60)$$

$$y = (KC_A^A - C_A^B)/KC_A^A \qquad (2.61)$$

In most cases $C_A^B << KC_A^A$ so that $y/(1-y)$ is a large number. However, the left-hand side is a very strong function of w going from 4 at w=1, to about 200 at w=2, and to 43,000 at w=3. Thus at an approximation we can assume that

$$\eta_X \sim \sqrt{D_A^B} \qquad (2.62)$$

Rudolph solves the diffusion equations for transfer of the migrant assuming that D_C^B, the migrant diffusion coefficient in the unswollen polymer, is a constant, but D_C^{A+B}, the migrant diffusion coefficient in the swollen portion, $0<x<X(t)$,is a function of c_A^B.

His result for the quantity of migrant transferred into the extractant phase per unit area at time t is:

$$M_t = 2C_{p_o}(t/\pi)^{1/2}/U \qquad (2.63)$$

where U is a complex function of diffusion coefficients and partition functions, but *not* of time. Thus, even in this case M_t is proportional to the square root of time.

To obtain more insight, however, consider the definition of U.

$$U = \frac{1}{\sqrt{\pi}}\ \frac{e^{-F(\eta_X 2)}}{\eta_X} E(Z) +$$

$$\left[\frac{2}{\sqrt{\pi}} \mathrm{Int}(\eta_X) + \frac{K''}{\sqrt{D_C^A}}\right]\left[K' - (K'-1)\, E(Z)\right] \tag{2.64}$$

where

$$F(\eta_X^2) = \int_o^{\eta_X} \frac{d\xi^2}{D_C^{A+B}(\xi)} \tag{2.65}$$

$$\mathrm{Int}(\eta_X) = \int_o^{\eta_X} \frac{\exp\,[-F(\xi^2)]\; d\xi}{D_C^{A+B}(\xi)} \tag{2.66}$$

and

$$\eta = x/2\sqrt{t}$$

$$\eta_X = X/2\sqrt{t} \tag{2.67}$$

$$E(Z) = \sqrt{\pi}\; Z\; e^{Z^2} \mathrm{erfc}\; Z$$

$$Z = \eta_X/\sqrt{D_C^B} \tag{2.68}$$

The calculation of U is very difficult, since, in eqs. (2.65) and (2.66), the migrant diffusion coefficient must be expressed as a function of η (i.e., ξ).

If one could assume a mean or average value of $D_C^{A+B} = \bar{D}_C$, and also that $\eta_X \approx \sqrt{D_A^B} >> \sqrt{D_C^B}$ so that Z is greater than about 2 or 3, then

$$F(\eta_X^2) = \eta_X^2/\bar{D}_C \tag{2.69}$$

$$\frac{2}{\sqrt{\pi}} \mathrm{Int}(\eta_X) = \frac{\mathrm{erf}\,(\eta_X/\sqrt{\bar{D}})}{\sqrt{\bar{D}}} \tag{2.70}$$

then

$$U = \frac{1}{\sqrt{\bar{D}}}\left[1 + \mathrm{erfc}\; W\left[\frac{1}{E(W)} - 1\right] + K''\left(\frac{\bar{D}}{D_C^A}\right)^{1/2}\right] \tag{2.71}$$

with the dimensionless variable

$$W = \eta_X/\sqrt{\bar{D}} \tag{2.72}$$

E( ) is defined in eq. (2.68). Substituting in eq. (2.63),

$$M_t = \frac{2C_{p_o}(\bar{D}\,t/\pi)^{1/2}}{1 + \left[\frac{1}{E(W)} - 1\right] \text{erfc } W + K''\left(\frac{\bar{D}}{D_C^A}\right)^{1/2}} = \quad (2.73)$$

Eq. (2.73) may be compared with Knibbe's result [eq. (2.43)]. The parameters ϕ and W are identical. The term $K''(\bar{D}/D_C^A)^{1/2}$ would be expected to be small and may be neglected. [It is, in fact, equal to β^{-1} of eq. (2.28).]

In summary, from both Knibbe's and Rudolph's analyses, where extractants penetrate polymer films, if a *mean* value of the diffusion coefficient of the migrant may be used in the polymer region penetrated by extractant, then

$$M_t = \frac{2C_{p_o}(\bar{D}\,t/\pi)^{1/2}}{f(W)} \quad (2.74)$$

with

$$f(W) = 1 + \left[\frac{1}{E(W)} - 1\right] \text{erfc } W$$

$$W = \eta_X/\sqrt{\bar{D}} \approx \left(\frac{D_A^B}{\bar{D}}\right)^{1/2}$$

For W greater than about 2 to 3, f(W) $\approx$ 1 and eq. (2.74) reverts to the simple case with constant diffusion coefficient and a well-mixed boundary condition, eq. (2.7).

While considerable liberties have been taken to simplify Rudolph's equations, the final results do suggest that analyses of migration in the presence of a penetrating solvent might be carried out using eq. (2.7), modified by the use of a correction function (still to be determined) of the variable ratio $(D_A^B/\bar{D})$.

Similar conclusions would be reached if the swelling case were considered (Rudolph 1980*a*).

Frisch (1978) has analyzed a similar case with concentration-dependent diffusion coefficients for the extractant and also predicts that the migrant loss is proportional to the square root of time.

4. PIRA Studies with Penetrating Extractants

Whereas the work of Knibbe and Rudolph were mathematical in character, the extractant penetration studies at PIRA in Great Britain are quite different. Adcock (1980) and Adcock et al. (1980) have described the results of their investigations over the last several years. Their interest has focussed on the migration of *nonvolatile* compounds in various polymer films using, primarily, binary mixtures of liquids to extract the migrant. In most cases the mixtures contained one component which was known to penetrate the polymer readily when pure. The other component was one which was essentially nonpenetrating, at least when pure, but one which did penetrate the test polymer to some degree when blended with the penetrating component. When possible, both components were selected such that, when pure, they each were solvents for the pure migrant.

The initial PIRA tests demonstrated that when only the nonpenetrating component was used, no significant migration of the polymer additive resulted. Weight-gain tests were used to prove the nonpenetration. The conclusion reached was that if there was no penetration, then there was no migration.

When a penetrant-nonpenetrant solvent pair was used to extract a nonvolatile polymer additive, some interesting results were obtained. To illustrate, consider the experiments carried out using PVC with magnesium cyclohexyl butyrate (MgCHB) as the additive and contacted by the liquid mixture of tetrahydrofuran (THF) and methanol at 20° C. THF is the penetrating component. Some migration-time curves are shown in Figure 2.9.

With 30% THF, essentially complete extraction was achieved after about one month. (For higher concentrations of THF, the extraction was completed in even shorter times.) Note that for THF concentrations below 30%, the percentage removal of the original MgCHB approaches an asymptotic value less than 100%. (In THF concentrations near 10%, essentially no removal of the MgCHB was effected.) These data are shown in a different manner in Figure 2.10. The ordinate is again the percentage of MgCHB migrated, and the abscissa now represents the percentage of THF in methanol. Two curves are shown, for times of 21 and 400 days. Presumably, for longer times there would be little change from the 400-day curve.

The asymptotic form of the migration-time curves is not normally found for volatile polymer additives. Apparently for nonvolatile migrants, the maximum quantity that can be extracted depends strongly on the

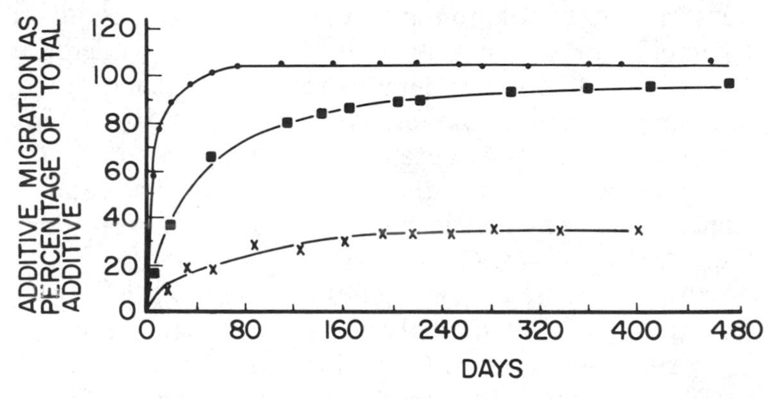

Figure 2.9—Migration/time curves for MgCHB in PVC exposed to mixtures of THF and methanol. From Adcock et al. 1980.

external solvent composition. Adcock and associates provide a model to describe this behavior, and it will be discussed later.

Various polymer-additive-solvent pair cases were studied with similar qualitative results. An important finding was that, even for the same polymer and additive, and with the same penetrating solvent, migration rates varied widely depending on the nonpenetrating solvent chosen.

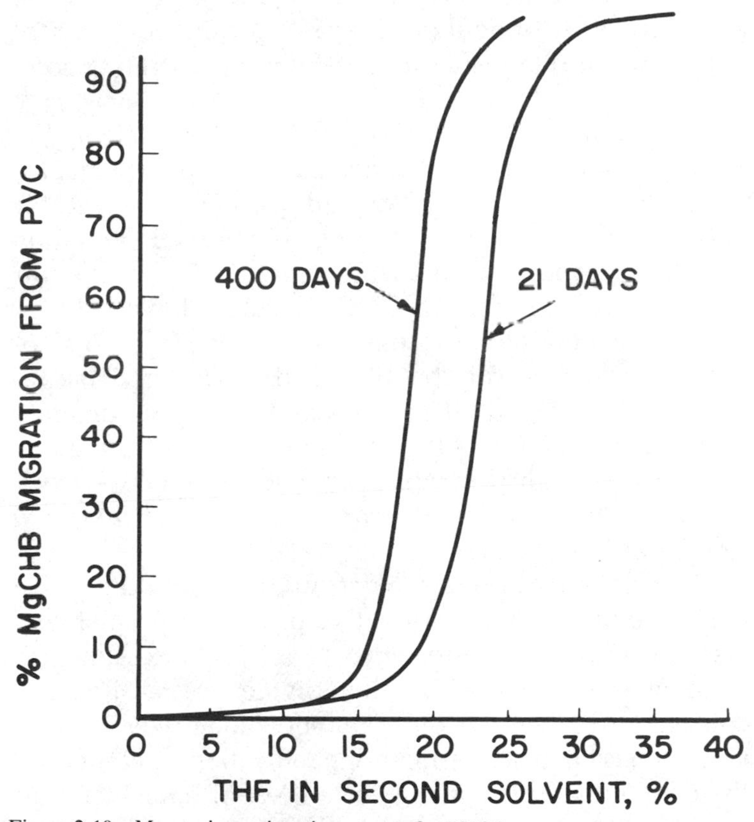

Figure 2.10—Magnesium migration curves for PVC in two-component extractants. Modified from Adcock et al. 1980.

In other experiments PIRA studied migration rates in cases where the migrant was present both in the polymer and in the external solvent mixture. As expected, the presence of high concentrations of the polymer additive *external* to the film greatly reduced migration rates. In a different set of tests, the solvent mixture viscosity was modified by the addition of ethyl cellulose. Migration decreased. It is not clear whether the decrease was due to local high concentrations of the polymer additive in the thin solvent film next to the polymer or whether the ethyl cellulose modified the penetration behavior of either (or both) the penetrating and nonpenetrating component.

In a few instances, after migration had been allowed to occur for some period of time, the polymer was microtomed parallel to the surface and sections analyzed for both the penetrants and for the migrants. Penetration was thus proved. Some data are shown in Figure 2.11 for the case of MgCHB in PVC contacted with THF-methanol solutions for 6 months. Essentially no loss of additive occurred for the 10% THF solution. Penetrations by the 15 and 20% solutions were approximately 0.18 and 0.48 mm. For the 25% solution penetration had extended through the entire specimen (2 mm). Adcock (1980) states that all MgCHB profiles *did not change with time after about 6 months*.

The fact that various solvent mixtures would remove only a limited amount of additive prompted Adcock and his colleagues at PIRA to suggest a model to explain such phenomena. In this model, the polymer was assumed to consist of domains of different molecular-weight polymer. A given penetrating-nonpenetrating solvent was then limited to enter only a certain set of domains. That is, there was an oligomer size above which penetration could not occur for a given solvent composition—

although this solvent could penetrate all lower molecular-weight domains. A solvent with a higher concentration of penetrating solvent was allowed to enter higher molecular-weight domains (and all lower ones). By pictorially placing the domain regions in a random manner in a two-dimensional grid, Adcock, Hope, and Paine were then able to visualize the degree of penetration for various solvent mixtures. Finally, by assuming that the migrant could diffuse out of the polymer only from penetrated domains, they were able to show qualitatively that

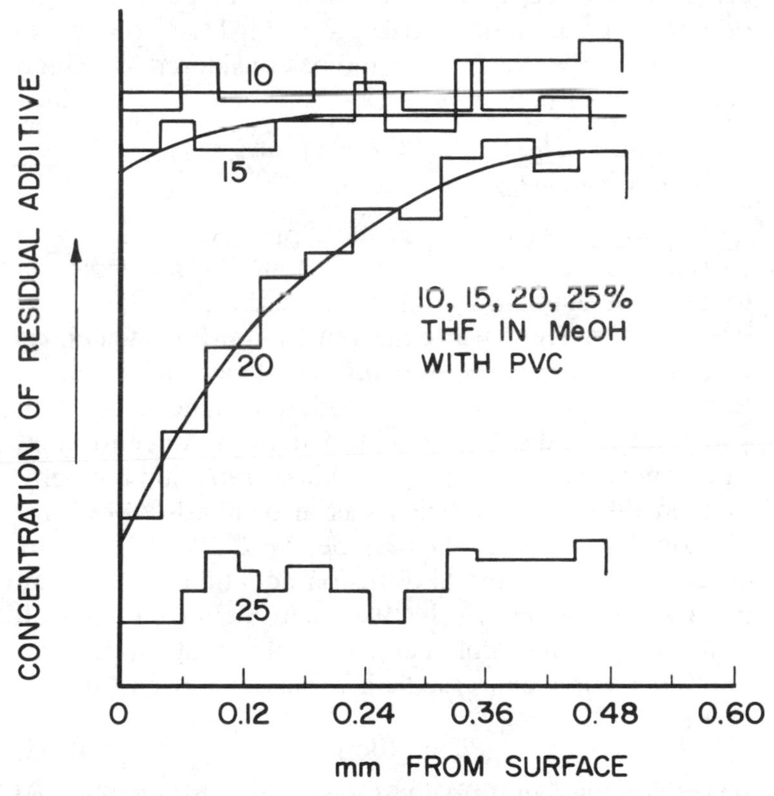

Figure 2.11—Concentration profiles of MgCHB in a PVC film. From Adcock 1980.

migrant concentrations as shown in Figure 2.11 would be predicted. Only with solvent mixtures that penetrated *all* domains would one be able to achieve complete extraction.

The importance of the PIRA study lies in associating the behavior of a real food and food simulant to the particular thickness of the penetrated layer. That is, it suggests that one choose as a food simulant a solvent mixture which yields the same penetration of the polymer as does the food. An example is presented for PVC in contact with olive oil. It is stated that olive oil penetrates the polymer to the same degree as a 5% THF solution in methanol. Thus, the latter could be considered as a simulant for olive oil.

5. Brief Review of the Current Literature Dealing with Penetration-Migration Processes

Pace and Datyner (1979) have proposed a theory to correlate penetrant diffusion of complex molecules in terms of fundamental properties of the penetrants and the polymer. They also point out that in the swollen region of a polymer, the diffusion coefficient of the penetrant cannot normally be considered to be a constant value but would increase with penetrant concentration. The importance of the polymer glass transition temperature on diffusion coefficients is also noted. Above T_g, diffusion is Fickian, whereas below T_g, it may not be described by the normal diffusion equations. This same point was made by Frisch (1980) in his detailed review on transport in glassy polymers. He notes that, in general, the penetration expressed on a mass basis can be expressed as

$$\text{Penetration} \propto t^n \tag{2.75}$$

where for Fickian diffusion (as assumed by Knibbe and Rudolph) $n=0.5$. For "Case II" diffusion $n=1$. In the latter, the penetration front moves at constant velocity and may involve stress cracking, swelling kinetics, and so on. No satisfactory theory exists to explain Case II diffusion. Frisch has commented on most models without reaching any definite conclusion. It is not clear, in practical cases, when $n=0.5$ or 1 (or intermediate values). Clearly, a better concept of pure penetrant diffusion into polymers is needed before one can assess the effect this penetration would have on the countermovement of a migrant. For example, to compare with Rudolph's results, if the penetrant were to enter at a constant velocity, then the migrant would not be extracted proportional to $t^{1/2}$. The rate would decrease with time with a different proportionality.

Wang and Duda (1980) have examined the penetrant-migrant diffusion problem and included convective effects. Only a few selected cases were considered, and these involved the movement of the penetrant from one side of the film to the other, while the migrant diffused both directions. It was concluded that if D (penetrant)/ D(migrant) exceeded about 100, then both diffusive and convective effects had to be included.

IV. Experimental Migration Data

A. INTRODUCTION

While many papers and reports have been published in the field of migrant transfer from polymer films, rarely are the data given in such a manner as to provide guidance either for understanding the migration phenomena or for testing a proposed analytical model (Haesen and Schwarze 1979). Therefore, many of the results shown in this section refer to recent experimental, unpublished work done at Arthur D. Little, Inc., in Cambridge, Massachusetts, which is under contract to the U.S. FDA to study the migration process using various polymers and migrants in contact with food and food simulants.

In section IV.B, I present experimental data for various tests and compare these results with most of the analytical models developed in section III. No attempt has been made to make this comparison exhaustive; the cases were chosen primarily to illustrate the good (or bad) agreement with the models.

In section IV.C, I introduce other data which, at the present time, are not well correlated by any model. In some cases I suggest a tentative explanatory hypothesis, and in others, I plead ignorance as to what is happening!

B. COMPARISON OF ANALYTICAL MODELS WITH EXPERIMENTAL DATA

Clearly the simplest model developed in section III was the case where the extractant was infinite in extent (or where partitioning did not occur) and there was so little migrant removed from the polymer that it too could be regarded as being of infinite thickness. Eq. (2.7) was the final result if no extractant penetration was allowed, and eq. (2.74), if penetration did occur. In both cases, the migrant transferred into the extractant was shown to be proportional to the *initial* migrant concentration in the polymer and to the square root of time. Figure 2.12 shows some experimental data for the extraction of styrene monomer from polystyrene into various oils at 40° C. An effective styrene diffusion coefficient of about $2.3 \times 10^{-13} cm^2/s$, with eq. (2.7), provides a good correlation.

Pfab and Mücke (1977) studied the styrene-polystyrene system at 70° C with sunflower oil. In this work, they were able to obtain some very early time data, and surprisingly, they found that the migration was, initially, linear in time and then, later, because proportional to the square root of time. No mention was made of any agitation. The linearity of migration with early time suggests that there may have been a significant mass transfer resistance on the sunflower oil side of the polystyrene film as suggested by eq. (2.41). If this hypothesis is assumed, then eq. (2.36) should be applicable to correlate their data. The short-time results were used to approximate the product of the mass transfer resistance times the partition coefficient (kK), and the long-time data allowed an estimation of D_p. With these parameters, the estimated and experimental migration results are shown in Figure 2.13. A reasonable agreement is seen from about 15 minutes to 10 days of testing although the "fitted" value of kK appears to be quite small.

Other studies have also suggested that early-time migration data were affected by external mass transfer resistances. Small (1947) and Quackenbos (1954) exposed plasticized PVC to flowing air and reported that

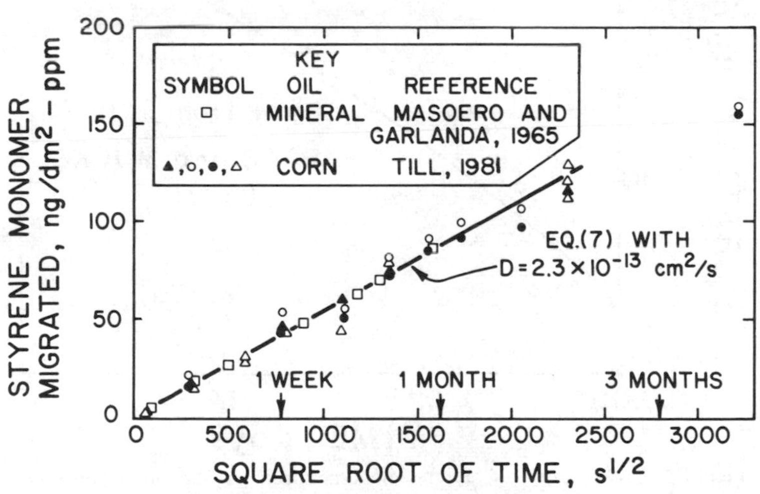

Figure 2.12—Migration of styrene monomer into oils at 40° C.

the plasticizer loss was initially proportional to time, but later became proportional to $t^{1/2}$. They attributed this behavior to the effect of a mass transfer resistance on the air side which, initially, was quite important, but, later, was negligible after plasticizer concentration gradients developed in the film. Kampouris (1975*a*, 1975*b*, 1976), Kampouris et al. (1976), and Kampouris and Papaconstantinou (1976) have made a rather thorough study of the migration of plasticizers from PVC to various extractants. In many of their test results, one notes that the early time data are nearly linear in time and again eq. (2.36) may be used. An example is shown in Figure 2.14. A good correlation is obtained; the difference between

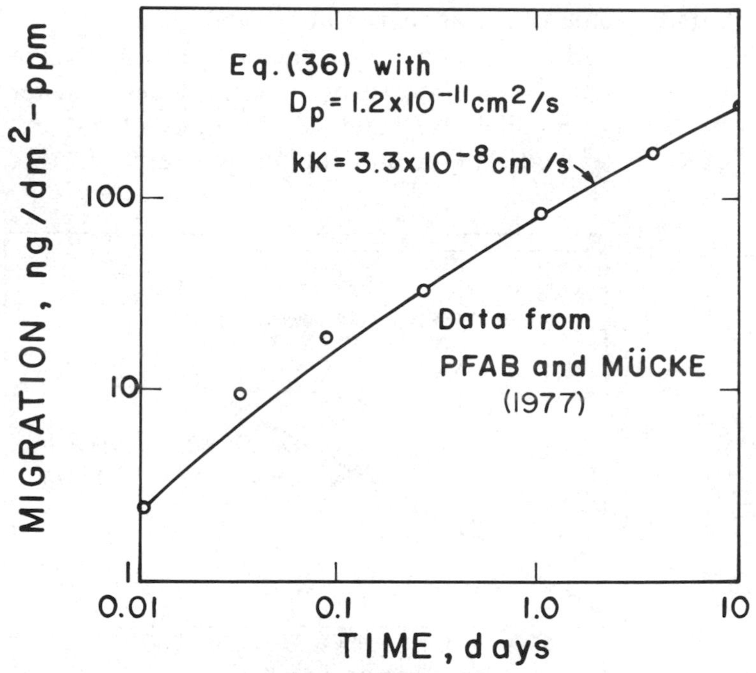

Figure 2.13—Migration of styrene monomer from crystal polystyrene into sunflower oil at 70° C. Data from Pfab and Mücke 1977.

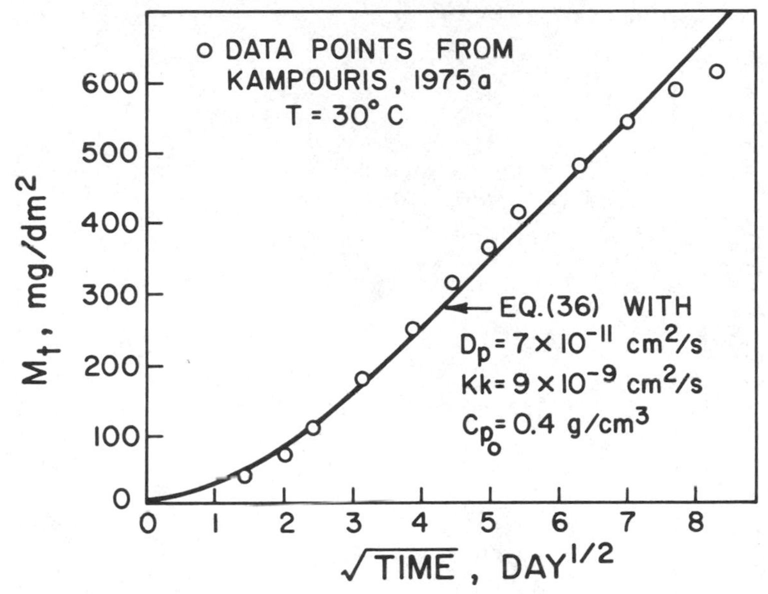

Figure 2.14—Migration of dibutyl phthalate from PVC into lubricating oil.

experimental and calculated migration results at long times can be explained by noting that so much plasticizer had been removed that the film could no longer be considered infinite in thickness.

Eq. (2.7), with no mass transfer resistance, may also be used for liquid foods, as shown in Figure 2.15 for BHT migrating from HDPE into milk at 4° C.

Still assuming that the extractant is well-mixed and infinite in extent, but in experiments where there is sufficient migrant transfer to essentially deplete the polymer film, eq. (2.14) should be used. In Figure 2.16 we show some migration results for BHT in HDPE at 40° C with corn oil as the extractant. Essentially 100% removal of the BHT has occurred after about a month. In section III it was suggested that eq. (2.7) would be satisfactory for values of $\psi < 0.4$ where $\psi = D_p t/L^2$. Since $L \sim 10^{-2}$cm

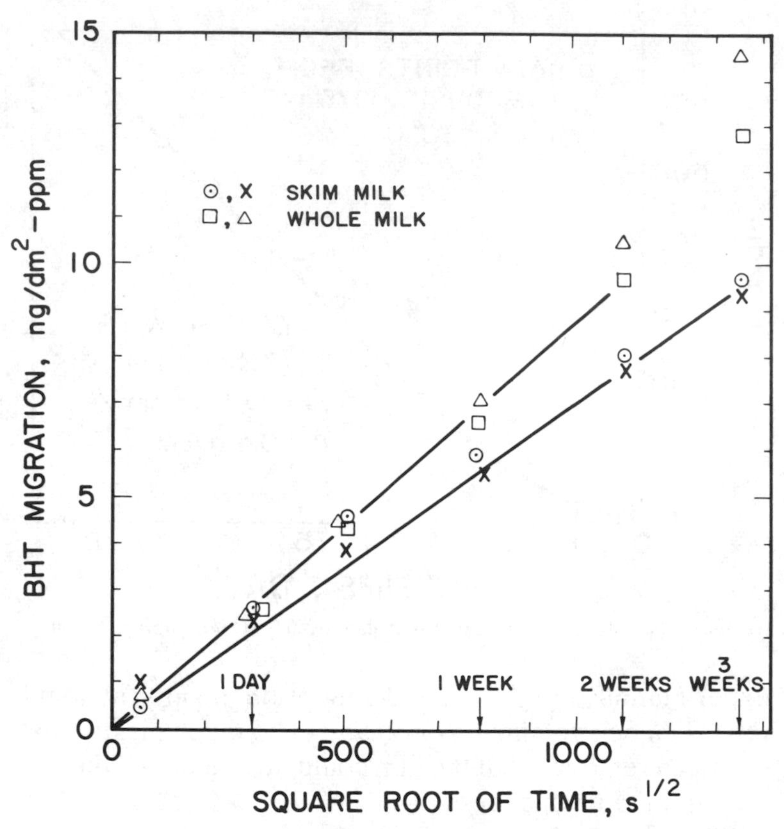

Figure 2.15—Migration of BHT from HDPE to milk at 4° C. Data from Arthur D. Little, Inc., 1981.

and $D_p \sim 3.7 \times 10^{-11}$cm^2/s, then $\psi \sim 0.4$ when $t^{1/2} \sim 10^3 s^{1/2}$. As seen in Figure 2.16, up to $t^{1/2} \sim 10^3 s^{1/2}$, the migration data are linear with $t^{1/2}$ [as predicted by eq. (2.7)], and only at later times must eq. (2.14) be used.

To illustrate the case where the extractant is finite in extent and partitioning may play a role, consider the case of styrene monomer migrating into aqueous solvents at various temperatures. All of the data were obtained from Till and associates (1981) except the 20° C water results, which are from Davies (1974, 1979). For this case, eq. (2.10) was employed. In Figure 2.17, we show the experimental results compared with the model equation. In plotting this graph, experimental values of the extractant volume / transfer area, a, were used; and the partition coefficient, K, was found from extractant concentration values at long times. The diffusion coefficient of styrene in crystal polystyrene was chosen to best fit the correlation of eq. (2.10)—but the values chosen were allowed to be a function only of temperature, not of type, extractant volume / transfer area, or initial styrene concentration in the polymer. For example, at 40° C, D_p was estimated to be about $3 \times 10^{-13} cm^2/s$. For water $K \approx 3.3 \times 10^{-4}$ and $a = 0.31$ cm; then with the criterion given by eq. (2.11), one would predict that when $z \approx 0.05$, the time is about 1 minute. For times less than this, migration is controlled by diffusion from the polymer. At longer times, partitioning between the polymer and water affects the migration rate as shown in eq. (2.10). If a or K were larger, then partitioning effects would be delayed to longer times.

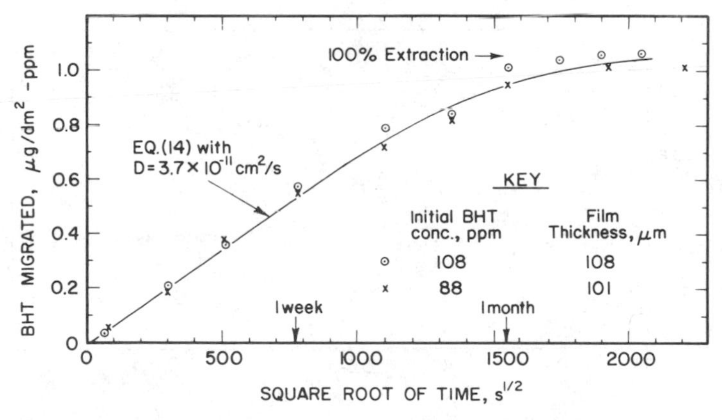

Figure 2.16—Migration of BHT from HDPE into corn oil at 40° C. From Arthur D. Little, Inc., 1981.

It is interesting to note that the value of the styrene diffusion coefficient in crystal polystyrene which best fits the aqueous solution (40° C) data in Figure 2.17 ($3 \times 10^{-13} cm^2 s$) is very close to the diffusion coefficient obtained with oils from Figure 2.12 ($2.3 \times 10^{-13} cm^2/s$). Since it is not expected that aqueous solvents penetrate crystalline polystyrene, the agreement between these two diffusion coefficients suggests that a value of $\approx 3 \times 10^{-13} cm^2/s$ may be close to the intrinsic diffusivity of styrene monomer in crystal polystyrene at 40° C. Masoero and Garlanda (1965) and Garlanda and Masoero (1966) also indicate that the diffusion coefficients of styrene monomer from crystal polystyrene into both water and oils are about equal at 40° C. (This was not true, however, for impact-grade polystyrene.) Using a rigid PVC and following the migration of vinyl chloride monomer into sunflower oil and 3% acetic acid, Pfab and Mücke (1977) report almost identical diffusion coefficients of the monomer in the PVC with both solvents. Thus, in a few cases, but certainly not most, migration from glassy polymers may be considered to be essential-

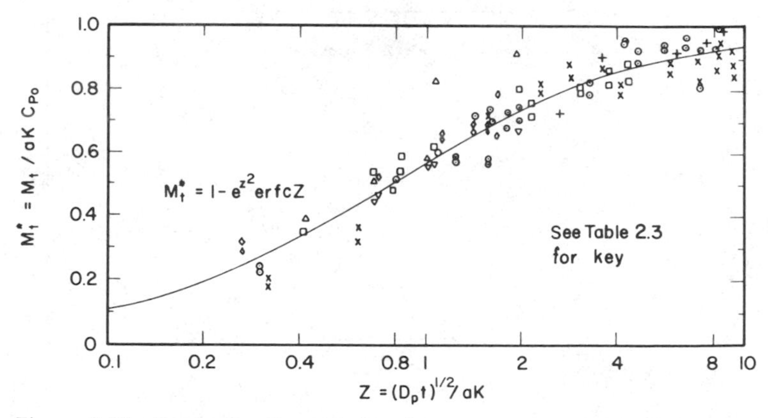

Figure 2.17—Generalized correlation for styrene monomer migration to aqueous food–simulating liquids.

Table 2.3. Styrene Migration into Aqueous Solvents: Values of D_p and K for Equation (2.10)

Solvent	T (°C)	C_{p_o} (ppm)	D_p (cm^2/s)	K	a (cm)	Symbol*
Water	4	800	5×10^{-16}	8×10^{-5}	0.31	◇
	20	700	1.3×10^{-14}	1.6×10^{-4}	0.50	□
	20	2,400	1.3×10^{-14}	1.6×10^{-4}	0.50	▽
	20	4,100	1.3×10^{-14}	1.6×10^{-4}	0.50	△
	40	200	3×10^{-13}	3.3×10^{-4}	0.31	○
	40	800	3×10^{-13}	3.3×10^{-4}	0.31	×
	40	3,700	3×10^{-13}	3.3×10^{-4}	0.31	+
3% acetic acid	40	800	3×10^{-13}	4.2×10^{-4}	0.31	⊕
8% ethanol	40	800	3×10^{-13}	6.4×10^{-4}	0.31	⊠
30% ethanol	40	800	1.5×10^{-12}	1.9×10^{-3}	0.31	∗
50% ethanol	40	800	5×10^{-12}	7.1×10^{-3}	0.31	⊖

SOURCES: Till et al. 1981; Davies 1974, 1979.
*Symbols are those shown in Figure 2.17.

ly independent of the solvent except insofar as the solvent may become saturated and equilibrium partitioning affects the results.

Figge and Rudolph (1979) studied the migration of BHT from HDPE with the penetrating extractant tricaprylin. By microtoming the HDPE after various degrees of extraction, they were able to determine the concentration profile of both BHT and tricaprylin as a function of time and position. In the brief summary of Rudolph's analysis in section III, it was shown that the penetrant concentration in the swollen region, c_A^B, was a function only of the variable $\eta = x/2\sqrt{t}$. [See, for example, eq. (2.55).] A similar conclusion may be reached for the migrant concentration in the unswollen zone (c_C^B) and in the swollen zone (c_C^{A+B}).

In Figure 2.18, these concentrations are shown plotted as a function of η. The value of n_X which denotes the boundary between the swollen and unswollen domains was determined to be 1.71×10^{-5}cm/s$^{1/2}$. Comparing Figures 2.18 and 2.8, $c_A(O) = KC_A^A = 17$mg/g, $c_A(X) = C_A^B \sim O$, $C_C^B = 1.82$mg/g, and $K' = K'' = 1$. The diffusion coefficients inferred from the theory and experimental data are

D (tricaprylin in HDPE) = 5×10^{-9}cm^2/s
D (BHT in unswollen HDPE) = 10^{-10}cm^2/s
D (BHT in swollen HDPE) = $10^{-10} + 4 \times 10^{-11} C_A^B$.

Thus the diffusion coefficient of BHT varies from 10^{-10}cm^2/s at $\eta = \eta_X$ to 8×10^{-10} at $\eta = 0$. From these data, it is apparent that the supposition from eq. (2.62) that $\eta_X \sim D_A^B$ is not particularly reliable ($1.71 \times 10^{-5} \neq 7 \times 10^{-5}$). (A much better agreement with eq. (2.62) is found in Figge and Rudolph's study of PVC-tricaprylin with the plasticizer Palationol AH as the migrant. Here $\eta_X = 3 \times 10^{-15}cm/s^{1/2}$ and $D_A^B = 1.8 \times 10^{-5}cm/s^{1/2}$.)

Figge and Rudolph also show the percentage of BHT extracted from the HDPE as a function of time. These

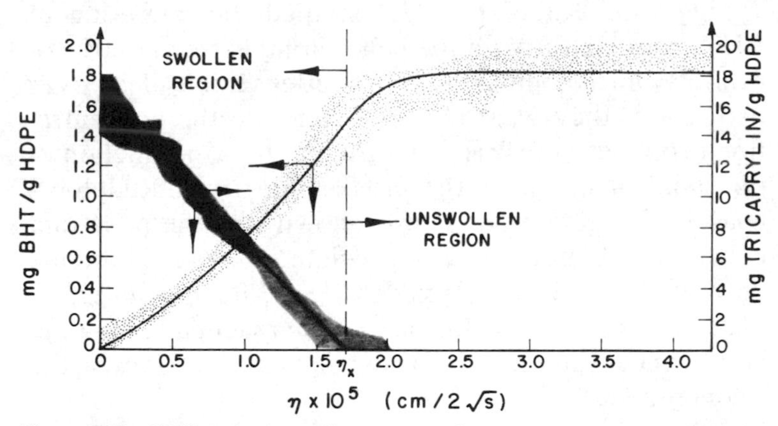

Figure 2.18—BHT and tricaprylin concentration profiles in HDPE at 40° C. From Figge and Rudolph 1979.

data are replotted on Figure 2.19 as percentage migrated vs. the square root of time. As expected, the data plot as a straight line to about 50–60% extracted and then tail off to reflect the fact that the center-line concentration of BHT is dropping. One can infer an effective diffusivity of BHT to be about $8.8 \times 10^{-10} cm^2/s$. This value seems somewhat high in view of the earlier comments about the BHT diffusion coefficient extremes of 10^{-10} to $8 \times 10^{-10} cm^2/s$ from the unswollen to swollen boundary. Nevertheless, Figure 2.19 does demonstrate that early time migration is proportional to the square root of time even when there is significant penetration by the extractant.

The last case discussed is that of an immobile solvent (or food). There are, unfortunately, few migration data

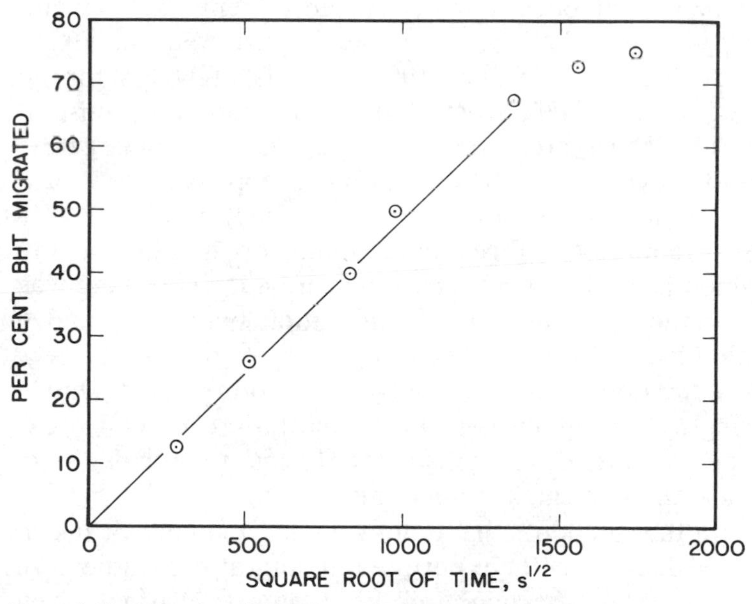

Figure 2.19—Migration of BHT from HDPE to the penetrant extractant tricaprylin at 40° C. From Figge and Rudolph 1979.

available for such situations. Till, Reid, and associates (1982) present results for the migration of dioctyl adipate from PVC into chicken-breast skin at 4° C. They suggest that the diffusion coefficient for this plasticizer in their PVC was about $2.3 \times 10^{-12} cm^2/s$. Also from the data, the parameter β [eq. (2.28)] was estimated to be about 0.92. If a reasonable value of the plasticizer diffusion coefficient in the skin is selected as $10^{-8} cm^2/s$, and an average a is chosen as $0.3 cm^3/cm^2$, then $K = 1.4 \times 10^{-2}$ and

$$z = (2.3 \times 10^{-12} t)^{1/2}/0.3 \times 1.4 \times 10^{-2}.$$

The longest test was 7 days, and for this time, $z = 0.28$. From Figure 2.4 at this value of z and with $\beta = 0.92$, it is clear that no partitioning effects are significant; and thus eq. (2.27) may be used. The term $\beta/(1+\beta) \approx 0.5$ would indicate that the migration is only about 50% of that which would occur if a well-mixed solvent had been employed instead of the immobile chicken-breast skin.

Arthur D. Little, Inc. (1981), reports a few data for the migration of BHT from HDPE into solid and semisolid foods. These are shown in Figure 2.20. For margarine and mayonnaise, the migration is approximately proportional to the square root of time. For vegetable shortening, the three data points do not lie on any smooth curve; for reasons which are not clear, there was essentially no measurable migration between 3 and 6 months.

Attention is called to the two dry foods studied. Only a single datum point is available, so little can be said except that there was significant BHT loss to both dry skim milk and dry chicken soup mix.

In this section, I have but sampled the current literature dealing with experimental migration studies. In many cases, the migration correlates surprisingly well with the square root of time until about 50–60% of the migrant has been extracted. (This holds for cases with little or with significant penetration.) When the migrant is only slightly soluble in the extractant, one must be aware of the effect of partitioning, as this phenomena can radically modify the migration process.

C. FURTHER COMMENTS ON MIGRATION MODELLING AND THE BEHAVIOR OF REAL SYSTEMS

Most of the examples presented in section IV.B were chosen to illustrate a specific analytical model. Unfortunately, in many other cases, existing experimental data do not seem to fit any existing correlation. A few illustrations are given in the present section, and certain other attributes of real systems pointed out.

One area of concern is to estimate the migration rates from plastics to dry foods. It was noted in section IV.B that BHT migrated readily from HDPE to dry skim milk

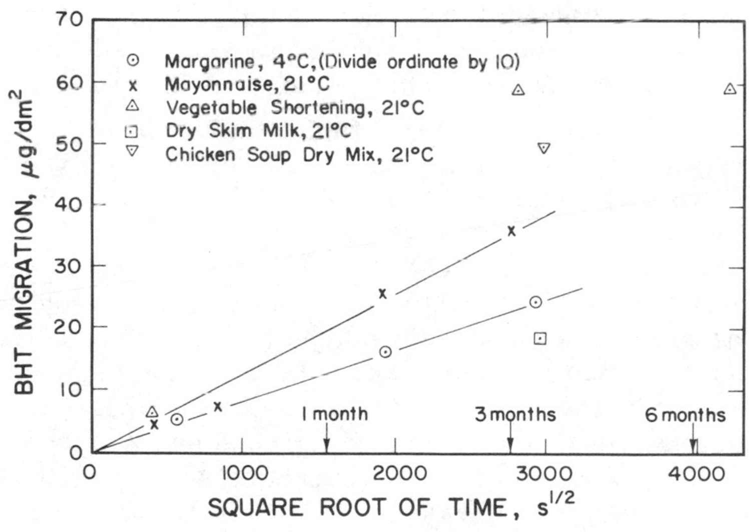

Figure 2.20—Migration of BHT into solid and semisolid foods from HDPE. Data from Arthur D. Little, Inc., 1981.

powder and, even to a larger degree, to dry chicken soup mix. Presumably, in these cases, transfer occurred largely through the vapor phase, but no model has yet been proposed to describe such a process. Figge et al. (1978) also noted that BHT would migrate from HDPE to medicinal powder and various kinds of tablets. Figge et al. (1979) reported that various additives in PVC migrated to dehydrated soups. Recognition of this phenomena has encouraged the European community to use as a simulant for dry foods a kieselguhr impregnated with the synthetic fat simulant HB-307. Clearly, more work is required to relate the migration rate to the properties of the dry food.

The state of the knowledge of diffusion of any migrant into a solid or semisolid food is very limited. Diffusion and partition coefficients are unknown, and thus it is not even possible to assess the relative importance of any mass-transfer resistances in the solid food phase. It is difficult to visualize the development of any satisfactory simulant for a solid food until the problem is better defined. Some examples will illustrate the point:

(*a*) Adcock et al. (1980) found that with a THF-methanol simulant, migration was affected by modifying the viscosity of the liquid with the addition of ethyl cellulose. Why?

(*b*) Arthur D. Little (1981) measured the migration of BHT from HDPE into three orange juice concentrations: the concentrate as normally purchased, a 3:1 dilution as normally used as a drink, and a 1.5:1 dilution to study intermediate concentrations. Somewhat unexpectedly, the migration was highest in the 1.5:1 dilution. Was there an effect of viscosity for the concentrate which reduced migration rates—while the 3:1 dilution had lower values owing to the higher water content? Or was there (see below) a more basic reason why the viscous, high-sugar-content concentrate was not a good extractant even when it contained the highest level of penetrating terpene oils? (See Phillips 1979).

(*c*) Till et al. (1981) studied the migration of radio-labeled styrene monomer to gelatin, vanilla frosting, and enrobing chocolate. Rates were very low. A partial explanation lies in the difficulty in preparing these materials for scintillation counting or combustion, and there could well have been some loss. Another possible hypothesis lies in assuming that the high sugar content of these foods was responsible. (Even gelatin contained 85% sucrose on a dry basis.) It is known (Chandrasekaran and King 1972; Menting et al. 1970) that in drying materials with high sucrose (or other carbohydrate) levels, a thin "skin" forms on the surface which is nearly impervious to organic molecules while allowing water to pass relatively freely. It is possible that similar skins developed in the gelatin, frosting, and chocolate near the polystyrene surface and that these impeded the migration of styrene monomer into the food. With this hypothesis, the sucrose (or other carbohydrate) content of the food may be more important in affecting migration than the fat or oil content. If such a hypothesis is correct, then it may also explain the low migration rates of BHT from HDPE to orange juice concentrate noted earlier. The high sugar level of the concentrate may also have allowed a very thin skin to develop, thereby reducing the permeability to BHT.

Another problem that is too often ignored relates to partitioning of a migrant between the polymer and extractant. Since most migrants are organic, partitioning rarely is important when using fatty foods or fat simulants. With aqueous foods or simulants, however, there may be severe problems in even defining a true partition equilibrium. Whereas pure water and water containing traces of a surfactant or an oil behave similarly in a diffusive process, there may be large variations in the partition coefficient (Reed et al. 1954). To see how this may affect migration, refer to Figure 2.3. The horizontal asymptotes for various values of α represent partition equilibrium. A change in the partition coefficient by an order of magnitude (which is easily accomplished for migrants that are sparingly soluble in water) will cause an order of magnitude increase in the fraction migrant extracted. The problem becomes even more confusing when one reads in the literature that saturation can even be exceeded (Quackenbos 1954—who studied plasticizers from PVC) with formation of small drops of the migrant appearing in the aqueous phase. No proved explanation of this effect is now known, but it can be readily appreciated that small temperature variations in the extractant could produce similar results.

In other work with the antioxidant BHT, Arthur D. Little (1981) found no partitioning with HDPE and water at 49° C. Apparently the BHT decomposed (or oxidized) rather quickly in the aqueous phase and never could attain the small concentration necessary to achieve equilibrium.

These examples serve notice that the concept of equilibrium of migrants may be elusive.

The effect of temperature on migration is clearly an important area, since most governmental regulations specify an elevated temperature to "accelerate" migration tests. We have seldom found that migration follows an Arrenhius behavior, although migration does increase with temperature. As the temperature rises, diffusion coefficients increase and partition coefficients may either increase or decrease. The effect of T on partitioning is seldom considered. Also, changes in temperature may modify greatly the polymer, particularly if it is near the glass transition temperature. Figure 2.21 shows a correlation of the diffusion coefficient of dioctylphthalate (DOP) in plasticized PVC as a function of the temperature difference $T-T_g$ where T_g is the glass transition temperature. T_g in this polymer may be changed by varying the percent DOP. For various test temperatures and DOP levels, it is seen that at high $T-T_g$, where the PVC is "rubbery," there is a *very* different effect of T on D_p than in the region where the PVC is becoming more rigid.

With these brief comments on the effect of temperature, I agree with Haesen and Schwarze (1979) that there is a serious problem in finding simulants to "imitate the migration in the most unfavorable circumstances of

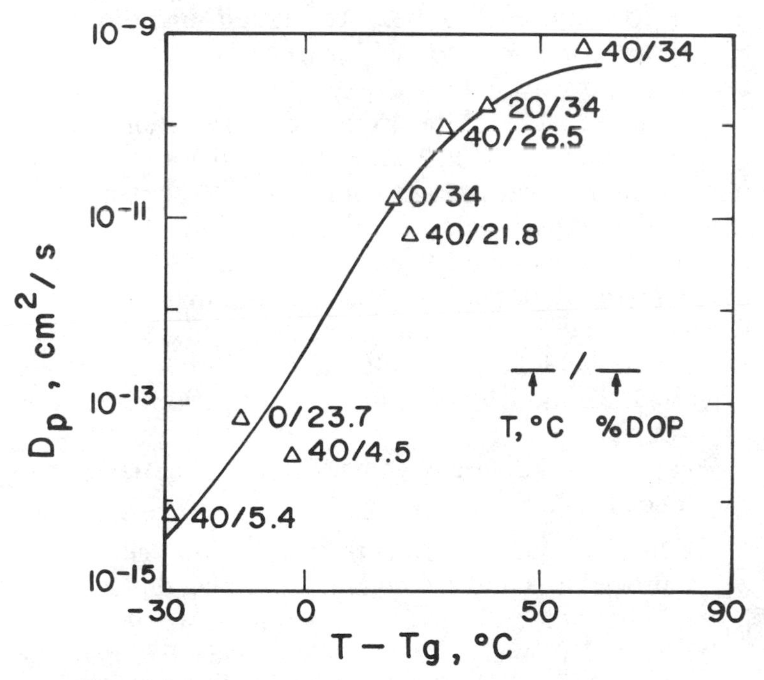

Figure 2.21—Correlation of D_p with $(T - T_g)$. From Pfab 1973.

use." Since many foods of interest have long shelf lives, accelerated simulant testing has become necessary. Rather empirical rules have appeared, e.g., 10 days at 45° C = 6 months at 25° C, or 2 days at 45° C = 9 months at −18° C, etc. Most European countries now use a 10-day, 40° C test to simulate room-temperature storage. The United States has a similar 49° C (120° F) test. Accelerated test requirements differ for different products—but it is not evident that the rules are based on particularly strong evidence.

V. Concluding Comments

The problem under consideration is to develop techniques to allow one to measure limited migration data *and* to have methods to allow extrapolation to the real use conditions for food-plastic contact.

The current state of the art is one of transition; we are far from reliable conclusions. Retrospective examination of much of the early literature forces one to conclude that few of the experimental studies are of much value in providing clues to the basic mechanisms (and problems) in the migration of polymer additives or oligomers to real foods. It is only very recently that theoreticians, such as Rudolph at Unilever, have attempted to provide realistic mathematical models for migration. Much more remains to be done.

Some of the key areas which cry for attention in the next decade are the following:

(*a*) International agreements relating to experimental procedures and methods of reporting data.
(*b*) Clarification of the concept of food simulant.
(*c*) Study of migration to solid, semisolid, and dry foods, with especial attention given to the anomalies now apparent.

(*d*) Development and testing of analytical models to identify and quantify the important experimental parameters.

We need courage, perseverance, and hard work.

Acknowledgments

My colleagues at Arthur D. Little, Inc.—Derek Till, Ken Sidman, Arthur Schowpe, Dick Whelan, and Dan Ehntholt—were exceedingly helpful in providing experimental data, critical and invaluable comments, and needed encouragement. Also Dr. Patricia Schwartz of the FDA was very generous with her time and expertise in formulating the concepts in section II.

Literature Cited

Adcock, L. H. 1980. "Better Food-Simulants: Are They Necessary? Are They Possible?" Paper presented at the Third International Symposium on Migration, Oct., Hamburg, West Germany.

Adcock, L. H., W. G. Hope, and F. A. Paine. 1980. "The Migration of Non-Volatile Compounds from Plastics," Part I, "Some Experiments with Model Migration Systems." *Plastics and Rubber: Materials and Applications*, Feb., p. 37. Part II, "A Descriptive and a Pictorial Concept of Migration." Ibid, May, p. 71.

Arthur D. Little, Inc. 1981. "Migration of BHT from HDPE to Food Simulants and Foods." Report to the FDA, Jan., Cambridge, Mass. Part of this report has been published: see Till, Ehntholt et al. 1982.

Bennett, J.A.R. and J. B. Lewis. 1958. "Dissolution Rates of Solids in Mercury and Aqueous Liquids: The Development of a New Type of Rotating Dissolution Cell." *AIChE J. 4*, 418.

Berg, N. 1980. "Sensoric and Instrumental Analysis of Off-Flavor-Giving Compounds in Polyethylene." Paper at the Third International Symposium on Migration, Oct., Hamburg, West Germany.

Carslaw, H. S., and J. C. Jaeger, 1959. *Conduction of Heat in Solids*. 2nd ed. Clarendon Press, Oxford.

Chandrasekaran, S. K., and C. J. King. 1972. "Volatiles' Retention during Drying of Food Liquids." *AIChE J. 18*, 520.

Crank, J. 1975. *The Mathematics of Diffusion*. 2nd ed. Clarendon Press, Oxford.

Crank, J., and G. S. Park. 1968. *Diffusion in Polymers*. Academic Press, New York.

Davies, J. T. 1974. "Migration of Styrene Monomer from Packaging Material into Food: Experimental Verification of a Theoretical Model." *J. Fd. Technol. 9*, 275.

Davies, J. T. 1979. Personal communication.

De Wilde, J. H. 1967. "Problemes analytiques posés par le contact entre emballages et denrées alimentaires." *Soc. scientifique d'hygiene alimentaire bull.*, p. 55.

Ehrenburg, D. O. 1932. "Mathematical Theory of Heat Flow in the Earth's Crust." *Univ. of Colo. Studies 19*, 327.

Eisenberg, M., C. W. Tobias, and C. R. Wilke. 1955. "Mass Transfer at Rotating Cylinders." *Chem. Eng. Prog. Symp. Ser. 51*, 1.

Figge, K. 1972. "Migration of Additives from Plastic Films into Edible Oils and Fat Simulants." *Fd. Cosmet. Toxicol. 10*, 815.

Figge, K., D. Cmelka, and J. Koch. 1978. "Problems Involved in and a Comparison of Methods for the Determination of Total Migration from Packaging Materials into Fatty Foods." *Fd. Cosmet. Toxicol. 16*, 165.

Figge, K., J. Koch, and W. Freytag. 1978. "The Suitability of Simulants for Foodstuffs, Cosmetics, and Pharmaceutical Products in Migration Studies." *Fd. Cosmet. Toxicol. 16*, 135.

Figge, K., and F. Rudolph. 1979. "Diffusion im System Kunststoffverpackung/Füllgut." *Angewan. Makrom. Chem. 78*, 157.

Figge, K., W. Freytag, and M. Baustian. 1979. "Selection of a

Suitable Test Media and Simulation Techniques for Checking Packaging Materials for Their Safety to Health, Part III: Migration of Additives from Rigid PVC into Foods and Test Media under Practical Storage Conditions." *Dtsch. Lebensm.-Rundsch. 75* (4), 118.

Frisch, H. L. 1978. "Simultaneous Nonlinear Diffusion of a Solvent and Organic Penetrant in a Polymer." *J. Poly. Sci.: Poly. Phys. Ed. 16*, 1651.

Frisch, H. L. 1980. "Sorption and Transport in Glassy Polymers: A Review." *Poly. Eng. Sci. 20* (1), 2.

Garlanda, T., and M. Masoero. 1966. "Constiderzioni sulla Migrazione di Componenti di Materie Plastiche in Solventi a Contatto." *Chimica e. Ind. 48* (9), 936.

Haesen, G., and A. Schwarze. 1979. "Migration of Plastics Additives from Food Packaging Materials." *Plastics and Rubber: Materials and Applications*, Aug., p. 93.

Holman, K. L., and S. T. Ashar. 1971. "Mass Transfer in Concentric Rotating Cylinders with Surface Chemical Reaction in the Presence of Taylor Vortexes." *Chem. Eng. Sci. 26*, 1817.

Kampouris, E. M. 1975*a*. "The Migration of Plasticizers into Petroleum Oils." *European Polymer J. 11*, 705.

Kampouris, E. M. 1975*b*. "Study of Plasticizer Migration Using Radioactivity Labeling." *Rev. Gen. Caoutch. Plast. 52* (4), 289.

Kampouris, E. M. 1976. "The Migration of Plasticizers from Poly(Vinyl Chloride) into Edible Oils." *Poly. Eng. Sci. 16* (1), 59.

Kampouris, E. M., and P. Papaconstantinou. 1976. "Utilization of Edible Oils as Secondary Plasticizers for PVC." Symposium 6, Lipchemie Industrielle, Proc. 13th World Congress, International Society for Fat Research, Aug. 30–Sept. 4, Paris.

Kampouris, E. M., F. Regas, S. Rokotas, S. Polychronakis, and M. Pantazoglou. 1976. "Migration of PVC Plasticizers into Alcohols." *Polymer 16* (11), 840.

Katan, L. L. 1979. "Migration Units and Dimensions." *Plastics and Rubber: Materials and Applications*, Feb., p. 18.

Katan, L. L. 1980. "A Generalized Dimensional Analysis of

Migration, and Physical Applications of This to Plastics for Contact with Food, Cosmetics and Medicinal Products." Third International Symposium on Migration, Oct., Hamburg, West Germany.

Knibbe, D. E. 1971. "Theory of Extraction of Additives from Plastics by Swelling Solvents." *Plastica 8*, 358, including Appendices from Koninklijke/Shell Plastics Laboratorium, Delft, The Hague.

Lovering, T. S. 1936. "Heat Conduction in Dissimilar Rocks and the Use of Thermal Models." *Bull. Geo. Soc. Am. 47*, 87.

Masoero, M., and T. Garlanda. 1965. "Sulla Migrazione dello Stirolo Monomero da Polisteroli." *Chimica e. Ind. 47* (9), 973.

Menting, L. C., B. Hoogstad, and H.A.C. Thijssen. 1970. "Aroma Retention during the Drying of Liquid Foods." *J. Fd. Technol. 5*, 127.

Pace, R. J., and A. Datyner. 1979. "Statistical Mechanical Models of Diffusion of Complex Penetrants in Polymers, I: Theory." *J. Poly. Sci.: Poly. Phys. Ed. 17*, 1675; (1979). "II: Applications." Ibid., p. 1693.

Paul, D. R., and S. K. McSpadden. 1976. "Diffusional Release of a Solute from a Polymer Matrix." *J. Mem. Sci. 1*, 33.

Pfab, W. von. 1973. "Diffusionserscheinungen im System Kunstoff-Fett." *Dtsch. Lebensm.-Rundsch. 69*, 151.

Pfab, W. von, and G. Mücke. 1977. "Zur Migration ausgewählter Monomerer in Lebensmitteln und Simulantien." *Dtsch. Lebensm.-Rundsch. 73*, 1.

Phillips, M. 1979. "Lemon-Tea Drinkers: A Group at Risk," *New England J. Medicine 302* (18), 1005.

Quackenbos, H. M. 1954. "Plasticizers in Vinyl Chloride Resins." *Ind. Eng. Chem. 46*, 1335.

Reed, M. C., H. F. Klemm, and E. F. Schultz. 1954. "Removal of Plasticizers in Vinyl Chloride Resins by Oil, Soapy Water, and Dry Powders." *Ind. Eng. Chem. 46*, 1344.

Reid, R. C., K. R. Sidman, A. D. Schwope, and D. E. Till. 1980. "The Loss of Adjuvants from Polymer Films to Foods or Food Simulants: The Effect of the External Phase." *Ind. Eng. Chem. Prod. Res. Develop. 19*, 580.

Rudolph, F. B. 1979. "Diffusion in a Multicomponent Inhomogeneous System with Moving Boundaries, I: Swelling at Constant Volume." *J. Poly. Sci.: Poly. Phys. Ed. 17*, 1709.

Rudolph, F. B. 1980*a*. "Diffusion in a Multicomponent Multiphase System with Moving Boundaries, II: Increasing or Decreasing Volume (Swelling or Drying)." *J. Poly. Sci.: Poly. Phys. Ed. 18*, 2323.

Rudolph, F. B. 1980*b*. "Considerations on the Relation between Polymer-Structure and Diffusion Phenomena." Third International Symposium on Migration, Oct., Hamburg, West Germany.

Shaw, F. B. 1977. "Toxicological Considerations in the Selection of Flexible Packaging Materials for Foodstuffs." *J. Fd. Prod. 40* (1), 65.

Small, P. A. 1947. "Diffusion of Plasticizers from Polyvinyl Chloride." *J. Soc. Chem. Ind. 66*, 17.

Smith, K. A., and C. K. Colton. 1972. "Mass Transfer to a Rotating Fluid." *AIChE J. 18*, 949, 958.

Till, D. E., D. J. Ehntholt, R. C. Reid, P. S. Schwartz, K. R. Sidman, A. D. Schwope, and R. H. Whelan. 1981. "Migration of Styrene Monomer from Crystal Polystyrene to Foods and Food Simulating Solvents." Paper Accepted by *Ind. Eng. Chem. Fundam.*

Till, D. E., R. C. Reid, P. S. Schwartz, K. R. Sidman, J. R. Valentine, and R. H. Whelan. 1982. "Plasticizer Migration from Polyvinyl Chloride Film to Solvents and Foods." *Fd. Chem. Toxic 20*, 95.

Till, D. E., D. J. Ehntholt, R. C. Reid, P. S. Schwartz, K. R. Sidman, A. D. Schwope, and R. H. Whelan. 1982. "Migration of BHT Antioxidant from High Density Polyethylene to Foods and Food Simulants," *Ind. Eng. Chem. Prod. Res. Dev. 21*, 106.

Vom Bruck, C. G., F. B. Rudolph, K. Figge, and W. R. Eckert. 1979. "Application of Diffusion Theory to Migration of Plastic Components into Packed Goods: Survey of Recent Migration Studies." *Fd. Cosmet. Toxicol. 17*, 153.

Wang, F.H.L., and J. L. Duda. 1980. "Analysis of Impurity Migration in Plastic Containers." *Poly. Eng. Sci., 20*, 120.

3

Creativity: A Sampling of the Psychological Literature as Applied to Graduate Engineering Students

> Now I really make the little idea from clay, and I hold it in my hand. I can turn it, look at it from underneath, see it from one view, hold it against the sky, imagine it any size I like, and really be in control almost like God creating something.
>
> —Henry Moore

Introduction

To provide a focus to this paper, I wished to address two general questions:

1. Are there well-characterized traits or biographical reference points to alert educators (and even recruiters) to potentially creative students?
2. What role does graduate education in engineering play in enhancing and/or suppressing creative talent? Also, in the same vein, are there practicable recommendations to modify aspects of graduate education to aid in the development of potentially creative students?

Summary

The diversity of definitions for creativity is noted, but the element of importance to engineers is that the event should produce a *novel* yet *useful* product (idea or thing). Creative products for engineers are usually the result of well-defined needs, whereas for artists and others they more appropriately represent an external expression of an inner self.

The usual sequence in the creative process is described in some detail—i.e., preparation, incubation, inspiration, verification, communication. The biological interpretation of the incubation and inspiration steps is discussed, and the conclusion formulated that creativity is largely gene-dominated. Stress is laid on ways creative ability, even that with a favorable genetic base, could be enhanced—e.g., by learning to observe better (and to note abnormalities), by attacking complex situations to "exercise the synapse," by rejecting conformity for conformity's sake, and, importantly, by recognizing the vital role of the preconscious mind so as to minimize the effect of debilitating neurotic problems. An example of the last point is Kettering's dictum that there is no shame associated with failing.

Psychologists continually attempt to relate definite personality traits with creative persons. These qualities are examined and most rejected. The two that do appear most appropriate are inner confidence and intense drive. I attempt to show that with these traits, one can develop other descriptors normally applied to creative engineers. Such characteristics are sometimes difficult to recognize in students, and of course, they are apparent in a few noncreative persons. I conclude that there are no simple ways to recognize creative persons and quote the old adage "the best predictor is past performance."

The use of psychologists' written creative tests is reviewed. Very little correlation is shown to exist between the outcome of these tests and a subjective evaluation of the individual's creativity as judged by peers and supervisors. Thus, the value of such tests is in doubt. I also question peer evaluation of creativity as a result of one study where peer judgement appeared to be based more on the goodness of the solution rather than its novelty or originality. All agree that IQ scores correlate poorly with creativity once a threshold ($\sim$120) has been passed. This conclusion may be more applicable for creative persons in the arts than in science and engineering, however. Most authors feel that biographical data can be of value in predicting creativity, but I could locate no convincing studies that would substantiate this hypothesis. I conclude that *a priori* prediction of future creativity in students is not possible.

The last section of the report deals with studies on how our education process enhances or suppresses creative talent. In essentially all cases, the educational process is damned as being too convergent, constrictive, or narrow, so that suppression leads to the rejection of science and engineering by many potentially creative persons. While I agree with many of these accusations, one can plead a viable defense on the basis of a cost-benefit analysis—and in light of the frugal attitudes of all college administrations, little could be expected if major changes in engineering education were to be proposed. It does seem possible, however, to develop small programs to increase the *awareness* of the creativity among both engineering students and faculty, and this theme is developed.

Creativity, I conclude, is a wondrous, complex, baffling phenomenon.

> Personally, I would sooner have written *Alice in Wonderland* than the whole *Encyclopedia Britannica*.
>
> —Stephen Leacock

Definition and Concept of Creativity

A simple, acceptable definition of creativity is elusive. While most psychologists do attempt a definition of what they perceive as creativity, most definitions are disparate. Some reconciliation is nevertheless possible by noting that some definitions emphasize the product, others the process, while a third class concentrate on the person. (These have been abbreviated as the P-P-P trilogy.) As an illustration, MacKinnon (1967*b*) states that creativity is a response that is novel or at least statistically infrequent *and*, in addition, is "adaptive to reality," or useful. A definition which is much broader and relates to the "creative process" is given by Torrance (1966): "a process of becoming sensitive to problems, deficiencies, gaps in knowledge, missing elements, disharmonies, and so on; identifying the difficulty; searching for solutions, making guesses or formulating hypotheses about the deficiencies; testing and retesting these hypotheses . . . and finally communicating the results."

Mednick (1962) presents a definition similar to MacKinnon's but places a qualitative ranking on creativity by noting that "the more remote the elements of a new combination [of ideas], the more creative the solution."

In contrast, the famous psychologist Guilford (1959) never formally defines creativity but instead proposes that creative performances be identified as fitting within a scheme of "divergent-production" operations. Getzels and Jackson (1962) extend this in "defining" creativity by judging the performance of an individual in a series of paper and pencil tests on word association, new uses for things, unusual interpretation of shapes, and so on.

The MacKinnon definition clearly seems to be most applicable to our interests: a novel response that is useful. Of course, one has to have some basis for a norm:

what is novel and useful to one group may not be to another, for the idea may already be known or the "use" considered bizarre.

And, while the simplistic definition of creativity given above may be valid for engineers, there have been suggestions that creativity for artists, musicians, poets, and writers may be very different. For the latter, MacKinnon (1967*a*) feels that creativity is an expression of the inner state of the creator, who externalizes something of himself into the public. For the former, the created product is more or less unrelated to the creator, who, in creating, plays the role of a mediator between externally defined needs and goals; in other words, the novel result is not identified with the "inner guts" of the creator.

Whether this distinction is valid or a gross oversimplification is an interesting question, but not particularly mundane to our current objective. I note it here primarily because many authors disassociate artists from engineers in discussing creativity. The one technical profession which is included within both groups is that of an architect.

Thinking and the Creative Process

Some time ago Poincaré succinctly described the creative process by the order "work-rest-inspiration-verify." Subsequent investigators have expanded and elaborated on this sequence, but many aspects remain unclarified. Crosby (1968) provides a particularly good discussion of the steps:

Preparation. The problem of interest is attacked. An intense motivation develops, and one drives oneself to explore all avenues. Passive thinking is minimized. In this phase, the definition of the problem of interest may be modified as limits are perceived, as one moves from a specific question to one of more generality.* Data are gathered, and the background (literature, earlier work) is explored. The mind is presumed to have an "active receptiveness." Convergent thought to "familiar" solutions is (or should be) avoided. Rather, by employing analogues, by projecting old concepts, by expanding the scope to cover peripheral topics, even by day-dreaming,† a broad grasp of the problem is attained. A solution to the original problem may, of course, be found during this initial stage. And it may be a "creative" solution as defined by the criteria stated earlier. But frustrations from being unsuccessful are often painfully evident; it is here that the momentum of the initial drive must be such as to allow further exploration. After such a period, one is then prepared to enter the incubation phase.

Incubation. Little is understood of this phase, although I shall suggest a biological interpretation later. The idea seems to be to stop "active" work on the problem and to allow mental process other than the conscious to assume command. Many authors suggest that success in this stage is enhanced if other mental tasks are avoided, i.e., it is recommended that one force oneself to deal with simple and familiar jobs. Other authors recommend alternate periods of intense concentration on the problem and complete relaxation. Next, if one is fortunate, there is illumination.

Illumination. Characterized in the comics by the light bulb shining overhead, the illumination step is an amazing phenomenon. Most of us have experienced it in various degrees. While *not* thinking about a problem we

*The following is often given as an example: the original problem was to develop a better can opener; the final problem was to overcome difficulties in opening cans.

†Freud is quoted as saying, "*No* doesn't exist in dreams."

have failed to resolve, suddenly there is an intrusion into our consciousness of a gleam of a new idea. This idea may be modest indeed and not solve the problem, but it may nevertheless suggest a potentially fruitful new approach. In such a case we revert to the preparation step for further work. Or, elements of a possible solution may be recognized in this step. If so, caution must be thrown to the winds to avoid a rejection. In this case one moves to the next step of verification.

Verification. It is in this step that one tests and develops the new idea. If it fails to solve the problem, one backtracks again to the preparation step, it is to be hoped still with some of the original drive. If the new idea succeeds in solving the problem, then the last phase is entered: the solution is communicated.

Communication. Most authors dealing with creativity do not mention this step. Yet, from my experience, creative individuals need to tell others of their success, to argue, to fine-tune their ideas. Papers, seminars, patents, and so on are logical outputs from this step. One psychologist noted the difference between scholars and creative people by saying that the scholar enjoyed contemplating history while the creative person was driven to make it.

With this brief summary of the creative process, we might return to some of the steps and emphasize certain concepts that could be significant in developing latent creativity.

One issue that has particular attraction is that of developing the appropriate perception and judgement in preparing for a problem—or, in fact, for future, unrecognized problems. The simplistic phrase to describe the general problem is, You see but you don't. How good are we as observers when we interact with people, when we carry out experiments, when we analyze data? Most of us have both mental and physical blinders which limit our thoughts and senses to what we want or expect. Few of us are sensitive to abnormalities—which are often the key to new findings. We are beset in coping with the everyday repetitive problems, so that, too often, we prejudge or grope to match new patterns with those we have known before.

We often do our best to avoid complexities. But many investigators believe that the complex situation is one ideally suited for the creative individual. I shall comment further on this later, but for the present, I simply note that our reaction to complex situations is too often to modify them to fit some organization(s) of past experience rather than to appreciate the "richness" of the chaos and to plunge in to unravel the problem.

Another point to be developed later is conformity. I simply draw attention to it as a trait which clearly inhibits the creation process. Being a noncomformist has, somehow, a bad connotation, but one must obviously be one to be creative!

In regard to the elements of the creative process, Golovin (1963) published a provocative article relating creative thought to thinking by a somewhat qualitative argument. Without going into detail, he stressed that the mental storage process is surprisingly efficient in most "intelligent" people. The mind has some 10^{10} neurons, with each neuron affecting about 100 others. Any "original thoughts" necessitates extended scanning in a mode not recognizable to the conscious mind. He suggests that the incubation step noted earlier involves random scanning in the subconscious in an effort to develop novel solutions to the existing problem. Such a process (as noted earlier) is undoubtedly more efficient when there is minimum interference with the scanning. The significant conclusion from Golovin's hypothesis is that creative thinking is then highly dependent on the individual's neural patterns, to the sensitivity of the neurons to fire, and to the rigidity and comprehensiveness of the reflex patterns of the neural system. In other words, he stated that creativity *requires* a central nervous system with especially efficient neuron action, and with a cortex which will not reject new (or unusual) patterns. On this basis, creativity could be said to be gene-determined; you have it or you don't.

An obvious corollary would appear to be that even if one has the requisite genetic characteristics, one still may not be productively creative. Creativity could be enhanced, however, by "exercising" the system to strengthen the synapse. Golovin likens the situation to that of a superathlete. The ability to perform is highly gene-dependent, but the performance itself is strongly related to the training. It is possible that such training could be an important element in our educational system for increasing our output of creative individuals.

Another enlightening paper, by Kubie (1967), presents a very detailed analysis of the conscious, the preconscious, and the unconscious thought processes. The conscious is that of which we are aware; little thinking is accomplished here. Operations are pedantic and are such as to react but not to analyze. The unconscious part (if I interpret Kubie correctly) is primarily a data base which may be tapped. The preconscious, to Kubie, is the important element in creativity. It is the scan element of Golovin. Operating almost continuously and quite efficiently, it is the part of the mind that solves problems, leads to new ideas, and provides our intuition. It does not like to be interrupted by the conscious, as this interferes with its function.

Kubie also argues that it is the preconscious that is most significantly affected by neurotic problems. Stress, worry, trauma, and so on lessen the efficacy of the preconscious. In a humorous vein, he suggests that creative individuals can neither be too efficient or too inefficient. The former make too much use of the preconscious to get things done on time, while the latter never get anything done at all. In other words, he feeds that even if one has great potential for being creative, this ability can be smothered if we are not aware of the sensitive nature of the preconscious. If true, this conclusion could have an important bearing on our education and treatment of such individuals. I cannot help but quote Kubie with his delightful description of an "ideal" situation: "The ultimate goal is a mind well-stocked with mature data, that acquires erudition without becoming leaden, that can carry its erudition lightly, freely, and imaginatively."

Closing this section, I must note some cogent remarks made by Kettering (1959) on inventors and creativity. He felt strongly that an inventor could not take himself too seriously: if he did, he was not free enough to come up with novel ideas. Kettering also stressed that an inventor had to become accustomed to failing—and he pointed out that this trait was the opposite of the goal of the serious student, who wished never to fail. (*Ergo*, serious students do not become inventors?)

Personal Traits of Creative Individuals

The classic paper describing the personalities of creative individuals is that of Roe (1961), who suggested six primary traits which normally would be found in a creative person. Most later authors have simply amplified or slightly modified her proposed scheme. I can do little more!

The most prominent trait I have noted among creative

chemical engineers of my acquaintance is the confidence they have in themselves and their work. They are not "Bohemian or radical," as Roe states, but obviously they have a well-developed ego. I have found little evidence of arrogance (another often-cited trait), *except* when they encounter work in their own field which they consider shoddy. Then their high standards intervene, and they can be caustic and critical. This inner confidence, I believe, is interpreted by others in various ways. One hears that creative individuals have a "high tolerance for ambiguity," which I read as "this is an interesting, complex problem well worth my time to examine." This same self-confidence allows them to be called truthful, adaptable, or aggressive. Some clearly interpret the confidence as a dominance trait, or as being low in deference (McDermid 1965).

Another trait I have noted in many creative engineers is their depth. But this trait varies widely. Many are broadly read, travel extensively, have a broad knowledge of many things. A few at the other extreme are, frankly, recluses. But, even in this latter group, the creative person is extraordinarily observant and well-informed within his own frame of reference or his own special field. Some authors state that creative persons are more sensitive to others (sometimes this is stated in terms of such individuals being more feminine, if a male, or more masculine, if a female. Perhaps this is true for creators in the arts, but I do not believe this has any significant basis in engineering.

In a similar manner, I cannot agree with Cattell (1963) when he terms creative persons schizothymic—i.e., withdrawn, skeptical, critical, introverted. True, I have never met a creative engineer who did not disappear for periods of time to some retreat away from others, but this is necessary if one wishes to get anything accomplished that requires sustained concentration. (Of course, many "noncreative" people also perform these disappearing acts; we judge their comparative creativities by evaluating the output from both.)

I would tend to agree with most others that creative people have unusual energy. In some instances, it can be overpowering. As I pointed out in the earlier discussion on the creative process, intense drive is a necessary prerequisite for attacking any important, complex problem.

Many authors indicate that while creative individuals are somewhat nonconformist in their field, they tend to be conformist in other aspects of life. This conclusion fits with my observations.

I disagree with Buel's (1965) contention that a trait of creative individuals is that they overcommit themselves and, consequently, always operate in a time-bind. Good people, anywhere, are going to be asked to do many jobs, join committees, take responsibility for seminars, meetings, and so forth. Human nature being what it is, it is all too easy to say yes—and suffer later.

I do find that creative individuals dislike mundane responsibilities in their professional life. In particular, many single out "proposal" writing as being very disagreeable. I don't believe it is the actual proposal that is the problem; it is more subtle and involves the concept that they are placed in a marketplace to hawk their wares (ideas) to those who are (perhaps) inferior to them in the field. They would prefer (expect?) recognition (and funding) without the proletarian hassle!

MacKinnon (1967*a*) attempted to categorize the personal traits of research scientists into the eight groups shown below. He then compared individuals having these personalities with evaluations of their creativity by their peers and supervisors. As you read the descriptions, attempt to prejudge the most and least creative type.

Type 1. The Zealot. This man is dedicated to research

activity; he sees himself as a driving, indefatigable researcher, with exceptional mathematical skills and a lively sense of curiosity. He is seen by others as tolerant, serious-minded, and conscientious, but as not getting along easily with others and as not being able to "fit in" readily with others.

Type 2. The Initiator. This man reacts quickly to research problems and begins at once to generate ideas; he is stimulating to others and gives freely of his own time; he sees himself as being relatively free of doctrinaire bias—methodological or substantive—and as being a good "team" man. Observers describe him as ambitious, well-organized, industrious, a good leader, and efficient. They also characterize him as being relatively free of manifest anxiety, worry, and nervousness.

Type 3. The Diagnostician. This man sees himself as a good evaluator, able to diagnose strong and weak points in a program quickly and accurately, and as having a knack for improvising quick solutions in research trouble spots. He does not have strong methodological preferences and biases, and tends not to be harsh or disparaging toward others' mistakes and errors. Observers see him as forceful and self-assured in manner, and as unselfish and free from self-seeking and narcissistic striving.

Type 4. The Scholar. This man is blessed with an exceptional memory, and with an eye for detail and order. He is not, however, a research perfectionist nor an endless seeker for ultimates. He does not hesitate to ask help when blocked in his work and feels that he can adapt his own thinking to that of others. He is well-informed in his field and is not given to bluffing. Observers describe him as conscientious and thorough and as very dependable, but as lacking confidence and decisiveness of judgement.

Type 5. The Artificer. This man gives freely of his own

time and enjoys talking shop with other researchers. He is aware of his own limitations and does not attempt what he cannot do. He sees himself as having a special facility for taking inchoate or poorly formed ideas of others and fashioning them into workable and significant programs. Observers see him as honest and direct, getting along well with others, and as usually observant and perceptive and responsive to nuances and subtleties in others' behavior.

Type 6. The Aesthetician. This man favors analytical over other modes of thinking, and prefers research problems which lend themselves to elegant and formal solutions. His interests are far-ranging, and he tends to become impatient if progress is slow or if emphasis must be put upon orderliness and systematic detail. His own view of experience is primarily an aesthetic one. Observers see him as clever and spontaneous, but as undependable and immature, somewhat lacking in patience and industry, and indifferent about duties and obligations.

Type 7. The Methodologist. This man is vitally interested in methodological issues and in problems of mathematical analysis and conceptualization. He is open about his own research plans and enjoys talking about them with others. He has little competitive spirit and tends to take a tolerant view of research differences between himself and others. Observers characterize him as a considerate, charitable person, free from undue ambition; at the same time they report a certain moodiness and an occasional tendency toward complicated and difficult behavior.

Type 8. The Independent. This man eschews team efforts, and dislikes and avoids administrative details connected with research work. He is not a driving, energetic research man, although he does have a lively sense of intellectual curiosity. He prefers to think in reference to physical and structural models rather than in analytical and mathematical ways. Observers describe him as active and robust in manner and hardheaded and forthright in judgement. He appears relatively free from worry and self-doubt, but inclined to behave impolitely or abruptly.

Whether you agree or not—and I do not—the Methodologists were judged to be most creative and the Scholars the least.

I end this confusing section by noting (*a*) that all creative people are not necessarily alike, (*b*) that all creative persons have an obvious self-confidence which is reflected in their enthusiasm for the most difficult, more challenging problems, (*c*) that all creative persons have intense drive, and (*d*) that creative persons create. I had to add (*d*) because we all know noncreative individuals who still meet criteria (*a*)–(*c*).

Identification of Creative Individuals

Many papers and theses in the psychological literature have described studies whose objective was to "identify" a spectrum of creative individuals within a given organization, and then to "test" these persons with standard written "creativity" tests to determine if correlations exist. The identification step varies, but normally there are two components:

1. Peer and supervisory personnel are invited to rank-order individuals within their working group on the basis of creativity. Usually no definition of creativity is given at this stage, so that the ordering is obviously very subjective. This may appear rather sloppy methodology, but I have discussed this question with a number of indi-

viduals in industry and education by posing the questions

(*a*) Could you rank-order your colleagues relative to their creative ability?

(*b*) Do you have confidence in your ranking?

Surprisingly, the answer to these questions is a quite positive yes—even though, in many cases, these same individuals had varying definitions of creativity. Also, the published results by this loose rank-ordering show good agreement within the group (including supervisors) as to those who are creative and those who are not. Thus an "identification" has been established, although the basis of the process is not clear and most probably varies from individual to individual.

2. Creativity is also judged on a more quantitative basis by giving written tests and by examining the output of individuals—patents, patent disclosures, journal papers—relative to the norm of the group. While this criterion can be criticized from many points of view, the quantitative nature of the result has some appeal. (Clearly, this method is widely used in universities to argue promotion and tenure cases.)

To note some specific studies, McDermid (1965) gave some 75 engineers and supervisors standard paper-and-pencil creativity tests. Essentially zero correlation resulted from the results of these tests and the peer/supervisor rank-ordering process noted above. He concluded that the only real aid in indicating a creative person was that person's biographical data. This will be considered more later, but as he put it, "The best predictor is past performance."

Buel (1965) carried out a similar study with R & D scientists in the pharmaceutical industry and obtained similar results. He did note, however, that creative people more often than not showed a history of parental permissiveness—at least insofar as decisions were concerned. This conclusion was not found by MacKinnon (1967*a*), who detected no correlation between background and creativity in a detailed study of creative individuals in engineering, mathematics, architecture, and the arts. This author also concluded that it was most difficult to develop predictors applicable to students that would have validity in later life. Like most other investigators, MacKinnon found little or no correlation between creativity and intelligence (as measured by IQ tests) once an IQ value of ~120 was attained. As a note on this rather important conclusion, McNemar (1964) states that such a result is true for the arts but that in science and engineering, creativity and intelligence are more closely related. From my experience, I would tend to agree more with McNemar.

Sprecher (1959) carried out a rather extensive survey of creativity predictors for engineers in a large aircraft design plant. The two primary questions asked were

(*a*) Who (here) is creative?

(*b*) Why do you think so?

He also gave standard (Guilford) written creativity tests. One hundred seven engineers were studied. No standard definition of creativity was provided. The results were as expected from other similar studies—i.e., there was an excellent correlation between different individuals' ranking of others *vis-a-vis* creativity.* But there was very poor correlation between this rank-ordering and written test scores. I was intrigued by the answers given to question (*b*) above. Table 3.1 shows Sprecher's results as to *why* certain individuals were judged "creative." It seemed to me that the judgement was based more on the value of the solution than on its originality. This result emphasizes the problem of asking about another's

*Except from some supervisors, who often had very different evaluations.

Table 3.1. Why Engineers Were Considered Creative: Rank Order of First Nine Variables

Rank order	Frequency of mention	Description of variable
1	34	Produces comprehensive and generalizable solutions vs. sketchy solutions
2	27	Presents correct and appropriate solutions vs. incorrect ones
3	23	Produces many solutions or ideas vs. few solutions
4	18	Produces novel and unconventional solutions vs. routine ones
5	18	Produces some solutions or one solution vs. no solutions
6	17	Uses flexible and varied approaches vs. inflexible and narrow ones
7	16	Produces practical and valuable solutions vs. impractical solutions
8	13	Doesn't blame others vs. does blame others and antagonizes them
9	11	Is interested in solution of problems vs. avoids problems

SOURCE: Data from Sprecher 1959.

creativity. Too often, the standard varies and does not relate to the particular creative process we have stressed earlier.

Taylor and associates (1963) studied creative scientists. Most of their results were negative. They found no correlation with age, experience, freedom to publish, total education, involvement in professional societies, or other factors. There was a negative correlation between organizational ability and creativity, and a weak positive correlation between "total years in the educational process" and "effectiveness in completing paperwork." High academic grades tended to go with later overall productivity—but not necessarily of the creative type.

Barron (1963) experimented with creativity tests which consisted of examining and commenting upon different drawings. He stated that creative individuals (both from the sciences and the arts) preferred disordered, complex drawings to those which were simple and ordered. He expands this result to conclude that creative persons are more ready to abandon easy classifications and look for unseen possibilities, or as he more deftly states, "They honor the apparently unclassifiable with attention."

Bloom (1963) chose to study Ph.D. chemistry majors from the University of Chicago after graduation. He found that 70% of all later publications were written by less than 10% of the sample. He also stated that if a student has demonstrated an unusually high achievement in graduate school, then it is very likely that this person will continue to be both creative and productive. High, average, or mediocre performance in college may or may not lead to later creative performance. Bloom suggested one simple question for doctoral candidates that may have value to predict later creativity: What did you enjoy in graduate school? If the respondent stressed the subjects taken, the seminars attended, and so on, this person could be considered an unlikely candidate for later creative effort. On the other hand, if the student emphasized his research problem, and resisted the passive student role, this could be considered a positive indication of later creativity.

The last study in this sampling of the psychological literature is that of Crosby (1968), who addressed many questions of interest to those in industry who wish to hire more creative engineers. He too rejects intelligence as being of much value as long as the IQ is above some nominal level (everyone seems to assume 120). He places stress on verbal fluency tests as a good indicator of creativity (others do not agree), but he chooses as the most important indicator the ability to perform "divergent" thinking. I presume this implies that solutions to given problems are novel or different—which seems reasonable since this dovetails nicely with our definition of creativity. In one of his tests he chose two groups of scientists, group A, ranked highly as creative, with an average IQ of 127; and group B, ranked low on the creative scale, with an average IQ of 150. After many studies of these two groups, he concluded that the main differences in observable traits between groups A and B were that those in A had far more wit and humor, more freely expressed their feelings, but were "inferior to B in social habits."

Creative persons were said to be capable of regressing easily into fantasy yet could bounce back with ease. (One of the less routine, but highly valued, questions asked of young people in creativity tests is whether they ever had a fantasy playmate? A positive answer is considered a reliable guide to future creative performance.)

Crosby could find little relation between creative and noncreative persons and their environment. He felt there must be some correlation, but he could not locate it—nor have later authors been more successful.

He has a chapter entitled "Inferences for Industry and Education" which is quite interesting. Several of his more cogent points are the following:

1. Managers do not like too many creative persons in their group. (This is also borne out by my questioning of several in different companies.) Why this is so is not clear, whether because of competition, of the so-called "disruptive" character of creative persons, or what.
2. The majority of engineering problems are so highly structured that the engineers involved do not need to be very creative.

3. No foolproof method exists to test future employees for later creative performances. Many of the personality traits usually associated with creative persons apply to those in the arts; too little is known about judging creative potential in engineering.
4. Corporations tend to become inbred and often miss out on new employees who do not fit conveniently into the company mold. Crosby quotes Jewkes et al. (1958) with the following: ''Institutions will naturally place emphasis upon the formal training and academic qualifications of those they employ: they will therefore become increasingly staffed by men who have been subject to common moulding influences. There is a possibility of in-breeding from which the more eccentric strains of native originality may be excluded.''

The same accusation might be leveled at our universities in their selection of both faculty and graduate students.

What, in summary, can be extracted from these and similar studies? If I were to be charged with the hiring program for new engineers (or with the admission of new graduate students), I would change essentially none of the current methods now employed—i.e., I would look for those who are intelligent, have good grades, work well within a group, and so on. But I would also become sensitive to the few ''different'' persons who show some or all of the following traits:

1. High independence (sometimes reflected in letters of recommendation from the faculty research advisor which express exasperation as to the student's performance).
2. Broadness in background (even to the extent of apparent random sampling of many areas).

3. Erratic grade record, with very high grades mixed with some very low ones. This can sometimes indicate excellent ability when motivated, but independence and a "who-cares" attitude when not.*
4. Evidence of creative performance in student projects or theses, in participation in theatrical groups, etc. At least here is evidence of some creativity; it is then up to the next supervisor to direct the ability to projects of interest.

These persons may be rejected under current selection schemes. But from all we know, such individuals may represent the more creative among the graduating class. Quoting Kingman Brewster, "There is a correlation between the creative and the screwball, so we must suffer the screwball gladly."

Effects of the Educational Environment on Creativity

The educational system from kindergarten through graduate school is invariably singled out as the principal culprit in stifling creativity. Many authors have dealt with this situation, and I can but sample some key references. I shall also limit myself to the situation in colleges and universities and, in most cases, to graduate education.

Wiesner (1967) formulated a policy statement which I am sure he hoped would be the goal for M.I.T. In essence he felt that the university *should* encourage imaginative and unconventional thinking, and factual material should be minimized by using general principles and laws. The former I agree with; the latter causes problems if students come to feel that general laws will solve all

*As one of my creative friends puts it, "If it is not worth doing, then it is not worth doing well."

problems. Tom Sherwood used to enjoy giving open-ended problems, those with no definite solution but with *many* possible solutions depending on how one modelled the real case or how one chose the criteria for correctness.

Kubie (1967) takes a very negative view of the current situation. He quotes the dean of a major engineering school, who maintains

> that of this selected student body not more than five to ten per cent become creatively productive; that there are some who demonstrate a high absorptive capacity, but never produce ideas of their own; that there is little correlation between creativity and high marks, or even between creativity and the mere fact of survival through the engineering course; that forty to sixty per cent of all students leave because of failure or else drop out voluntarily in spite of passing grades, and that together these two categories of "drop-outs" include a major share of those with high potential creativity; and that our educational processes tend to destroy the creative potential of a large share of those who survive.

As applied to most undergraduates, I am in agreement with his view.

Sears (1964) in a delightful, brief address presents a point of view that has real elements of truth, but it is hard to believe he is serious. He suggests three definitive ways to improve creativity in the graduate school.

1. Improve graduate student selection. Sears is critical of our present method, which is heavily based on GRE scores, grades, conformity, and so on. He suggests, instead, we accent outside interests, hobbies, unusual biographical items, to better judge potential creativity.
2. Develop a *creative* faculty. He points out this

would provide role models; more important, creative faculty tend to be more liberal with their research students and would leave them alone.

3. Radically simplify the graduate school administration. His complaint here is that there are too many persons he calls "centralists," who exist by making rules and regulations (and enforcing them). More freedom would be conducive to the development of creative individuals.

Dr. Sears was dean of engineering at Stanford when he presented these ideas. In simplified form, he believed one should get the most promising students, provide role models, and leave each student more or less alone to develop as best he or she could.

Many authors criticize current educational methods as being too absorptive, too hectic. Miller (1970) aptly states that it is hard to learn to incubate ideas when you are always running. The degree of success in many subjects is measured by the digestion of facts, and little imagination is necessary to obtain an A. Or, as Kettering (1959) states, students believe the book far too much and don't appreciate the fact that there are no "books" for most real problems. Our Ph.D. programs are geared to those students who can take tests; there is no risk in doing well in book-learning.

These same points were made by Cattell (1963), who flatly states that tinkering with a curriculum will not aid in producing creative people. His key to doing so lies in developing personal value scales rather than in promoting cognitive skills. He also is critical of schools (*and* of industries who hire their graduates) for cherishing the extroverts. The pleasant, friendly, outgoing, reasonably smart person is far more desirable than the smart, but hard to know and understand introvert. The point he seems to be making is that introverts are more often creative than extroverts. That is a rather broad generalization that has many exceptions.

Kuhn (1963), who was both a physicist and a science historian, tried to examine the educational process for scientists in a broader context. He correctly points out there must be a blend of convergent and divergent thinking exercises to pave the way for the "preparation and incubation" steps of creation. He also notes the difference between the education of humanities majors and that of science majors, in that the former spend an appreciable time studying well-known creative people of the past and reading their works, whereas in science little historical perspective is ever developed. He suggests that creation in the arts comes about by different motivating pressures and by different routes than in the sciences—and he extends this line of thought to separate basic scientists and applied scientists (engineers?). He reminds the reader that Edison believed that basic scientists were "wooly-headed" and didn't know what was worth doing.

If Kuhn's arguments have merit, then could we conclude that creativity in applied science is a strong function of the problem? That is, one (presumably the manager) must be able to formulate the problem in terms of existing scientific tradition and to have a rather definite concept of what could be of most value in any solution. Such a statement would be far less applicable for directing basic scientists and would be essentially meaningless when applied to artists, musicians, and the like.

Although the educational system is held largely responsible for our failure to develop creative graduates, it may not be as much at fault as one supposes. In a study of creativity of high school graduates, Walker (1967) examined a number of shcools in a large metropolitan area. He chose to concentrate on the two extremes—i.e., the few schools who prided themselves on providing an environment conducive to creative students (high intellectual climate, active student participation, less authoritarian teachers, classes which encouraged initiative and originality, etc.) and schools which had few of these traits. Yet the graduates from these two types of schools could not be distinguished on the basis of standard creativity tests. Walker somewhat lamely concludes that "maybe the school environment is important, but existing paper and pencil tests do not show it."

In concluding this sampling of comments dealing with the education-creativity interaction, I have adapted some conclusions of Crosby (1968) that I feel are applicable to chemical engineering education.

1. Schools have traditional academic values, and these are not likely to reward most independent, creative students. But young students are easily stifled in their attempts at creativity by negative reactions. Rewards for trying might help, as success breeds success.
2. There is too much emphasis on selective intelligence testing, and the stress is on convergent thought (correct solution) rather than on cognitive precepts.
3. There are five noteworthy factors in our educational process which inhibit creativity:
   (*a*) success orientation: a fear of failure is ever present;
   (*b*) peer pressure: conformity is valued;
   (*c*) little encouragement of critical exploration: curiosity tends to be disruptive;
   (*d*) negative reaction to divergent behavior: the "you're a nut" syndrome;
   (*e*) development of the work (burden)/play (unrelated to work) dichotomy.

4. Finally, there is the continuum in which teachers tend to pass on to their students the schemata they themselves had learned (not the new, the unknown, the bothersome), and these students do the same if they become teachers.

Thus, a rather bleak picture is painted of most educational systems. In their defense one could point out that engineering faculty members are normally not promoted for their teaching ability, that small classes or one-on-one studies are too costly, that only the creative students need major changes made in the system (and how does one select those to be favored?). Still, with all the criticism and rebuttal, there do seem to be some things which might be done without overturning our current educational system. Two in particular are singled out here. Both proposals are aimed primarily at increasing the awareness of creativity. In my discussions with both students and engineering faculty, I have found an interest in learning more about the area. Therefore, I would like to see some mechanism adopted which would introduce creativity to both students and faculty—probably not at the same time or in the same way.

For the students, it would be best to have contact in several seminars both with an engineer interested in creativity and with a psychologist who has a better grasp of the complex overall area. The definition and values of creation could be discussed, and the creative process examined with concomitant comparisons of descriptions of creative persons. The problems of the graduate student in coping with conformity while still developing an independent personality and performing (creative) independent research would certainly be a principal focus. I believe that exposure of these and other areas of creativity to graduate students would allow them to appreciate their peers in a more constructive way *and*, even more importantly, allow them to analyze their own motives, drives, and personalities in order to become more productive, to avoid stifling of new ideas that may be radical, and to understand better the ups and downs of research as one probes complex and ill-defined projects.

For the faculty, an open and frank discussion of creativity (probably with a professional trained in psychology and specializing in creativity) would be most interesting. At the least one would hope that such a discussion would lead to a more tolerant and understanding attitude toward the independent, possibly creative, student. I would also hope that, in some cases, a better awareness of the ease with which creativity can be suppressed in students would lead to teaching and research supervision that encouraged more divergent thinking. In a few cases, awareness might even make the faculty member more creative in his or her own work!

There is, certainly, no guarantee that these pilot projects as proposed would have a particularly significant effect on the number of really creative graduates. As do most psychologists, I feel that the ability to create is largely gene-dominated. So we cannot *create* creative persons. But perhaps we can encourage those who already have the inherent ability to recognize and develop their talents. I, like many others, feel that we in chemical engineering do not encourage creative individuals sufficiently—in fact, in many instances, we "turn them off," and they go elsewhere in science or even into the arts where they find their abilities better understood.

Literature Cited

Bailey, R. L. 1978. "Disciplined Creativity for Engineers." Ann Arbor Science Pub. Co., Ann Arbor.

Barron, F. X. 1963. "The Needs for Order and Disorder as

Motives in Creative Activity." In *Scientific Creativity: Its Recognition and Development*, ed. C. W. Taylor and F. X. Barron. Wiley, New York.

Belcher, T. L. 1972. "Modeling Creative Behavior." Ph.D. thesis, Univ. of Wisconsin, Madison.

Bloom, B.S. 1963. "Report on Creativity Research by the Examiner's Office of the University of Chicago." In *Scientific Creativity: Its Recognition and Development*, ed. C. W. Taylor and F. X. Barron. Wiley, New York.

Buel, W. D. 1965. "Biographical Data and the Identification of Creative Research Personnel." *J. App. Psychol. 49*, 318.

Cattell, R. B. 1963. "The Personality and Motivation of the Researcher from Measurements of Contemporaries and from Biography." In *Scientific Creativity: Its Recognition and Development*, ed. C. W. Taylor and F. X. Barron. Wiley, New York.

Crosby, A. 1968. *Creativity and Performance in Industrial Organization*. Travistock Publications, London.

Getzels, J. W., and P. W. Jackson. 1962. *Creativity and Intelligence*. Wiley, New York.

Golovin, N. E. 1963. "The Creative Person in Science." In *Scientific Creativity: Its Recognition and Development*, ed. C. W. Taylor and F. X. Barron. Wiley, New York.

Guilford, J. P. 1959. "Three Faces of Intellect." *Am. Psychologist 14*, 469.

Jewkes, J., D. Sawers, and R. Stillerman. 1958. *The Sources of Invention*. Macmillan, London.

Kagan, J., ed. 1967. *Creativity and Learning*. Houghton-Mifflin, Boston.

Kettering, C. F. 1959. "How Can We Develop Inventors?" In *Professional Creativity*, ed. E. K. von Fange. Prentice-Hall, Englewood Cliffs, N.J.

Koch, W. E. 1978. *The Creative Engineer: The Art of Inventing*. Plenum Press, New York.

Kubie, L. S. 1967. "Unsolved Problems of Scientific Education." In *Creativity and Learning*, ed. J. Kagan. Houghton Mifflin, Boston.

Kuhn, T. S. 1963. "The Essential Tension." In *Scientific*

Creativity: Its Recognition and Development, ed. C. W. Taylor and F. X. Barron. Wiley, New York.

McDermid, C. D. 1965. "Some Correlates of Creativity in Engineering Personnel." *J. App. Psychol. 49*, 14.

MacKinnon, D. W. 1967*a*. "Identifying and Developing Creativity." In *Creativity: Its Educational Implications*, ed. J. C. Gowan, G. D. Demos, and E. P. Torrance. Wiley, New York.

MacKinnon, D. W. 1967*b*. "The Study of Creative Persons: A Method and Some Results." In *Creativity and Learning*, ed. J. Kagan. Houghton Mifflin, Boston.

McNemar, Q. 1964. "Lost: Our Intelligence? Why?" *Am. Psychol. 19*, 871.

Mednick, S. A. 1962. "The Associative Basis of the Creative Process." *Psychol. Rev. 69*, 220.

Miller, B. 1970. *Managing Innovation for Growth and Profit*. Dow Jones-Irwin Inc., Homewood, Ill.

Prince, G. M. 1970. *The Practice of Creativity*. Harper & Row, New York.

Roe, A. 1961. "The Psychology of the Scientist." *Science 134*, 456.

Sears, R. R. 1964. "Graduate Education and the Creative Process." In *Creativity in Graduate Education*, ed. A. B. Friedman. Claremont College, Claremont, Calif.

Semrud, M. E. 1975. "The Relationship between Creativity, Achievement Level, and Variability of Academic Performance." M.S. thesis, Univ. of Wisconsin, Madison.

Sprecher, T. B. 1959. "A Study of Engineers' Criteria for Creativity." *J. Appl. Psychol. 43*, 141.

Taylor, C. W., W. R. Smith, and B. Ghiselin. 1963. "The Creative and Other Contributions of One Sample of Research Scientists." In *Scientific Creativity: Its Recognition and Development*, ed. C. W. Taylor and F. X. Barron. Wiley, New York.

Torrance, E. P. 1966. *Torrance Tests of Creative Thinking: Norms-technical Manual, Research Edition*. Personnel Press, Princeton, N.J.

Von Fange, E. D., ed. 1959. *Professional Creativity*. Prentice-Hall, Englewood Cliffs, N.J.
Walker, W. J. 1967. "Creativity and High School Climate." In *Creativity: Its Educational Implications*, ed. J. C. Gowan, G. D. Demos, and E. P. Torrance. Wiley, New York.
Wiesner, J. B. 1967. "Education for Creativity." In *Creativity and Learning*, ed. J. Kagan. Houghton Mifflin, Boston.